# WEST MIDLANDS VOL II

Edited by Allison Dowse

First published in Great Britain in 2000 by
*YOUNG WRITERS*
Remus House,
Coltsfoot Drive,
Woodston,
Peterborough, PE2 9JX
Telephone (01733) 890066

HB ISBN 0 75432 088 X
SB ISBN 0 75432 089 8

# FOREWORD

This year, the Young Writers' Up, Up & Away competition proudly presents a showcase of the best poetic talent from over 70,000 up-and-coming writers nationwide.

Successful in continuing our aim of promoting writing and creativity in children, our regional anthologies give a vivid insight into the thoughts, emotions and experiences of today's younger generation, displaying their inventive writing in its originality.

The thought, effort, imagination and hard work put into each poem impressed us all and again the task of editing proved challenging due to the quality of entries received, but was nevertheless enjoyable. We hope you are as pleased as we are with the final selection and that you continue to enjoy *Up, Up & Away West Midlands Vol II*.for many years to come.

# CONTENTS

| | |
|---|---|
| Alice Davies | 19 |
| Alexander Harris | 20 |
| Sophie Freeman | 20 |
| Matthew Clarke | 20 |
| Sara Mason | 21 |
| Rebecca Jackson | 21 |
| Harriet Brough | 21 |
| Matthew Guy | 22 |
| Oliver Deeley | 22 |
| Suzanne Nickl | 22 |
| Laura Caswell | 23 |
| Carl Phillips | 23 |
| Sarah Turner | 23 |
| Colin Oliver | 24 |

### Gig Mill Primary School

| | |
|---|---|
| Samantha Parkes | 24 |
| Bethan Hughes | 25 |
| Laura Godwin | 25 |
| Charlotte Rudge | 26 |
| Emma Stewart | 27 |
| Danielle Emery | 27 |
| Kate Holtham | 28 |
| Helen Irwin | 29 |
| Nicola Leiper | 29 |

### Hob Green Primary School

| | |
|---|---|
| Melanie Jastrzebski | 30 |
| Alex Downing | 30 |
| Sarah Louise Jordan | 31 |
| Sarah Curtis | 31 |
| Laura Collins | 32 |
| Adam Johnson | 32 |
| Cherelle Bashford | 33 |
| John Webb | 34 |
| Rachael Perry | 34 |
| Nicholas Johnson | 34 |
| Kelly Davies | 35 |

Lucy Moore 57
Jade Thistlethwaite 57

King's Hill Primary School
Kelly Bowater 58
Emma Dolman 58
Abu Taher 59
Jade Bristow 59
Dionne Phipps 60
Chrisopher Perry 60

Mount Pleasant Primary School
Lewis Mason 61
Thomas Houghton 61
Abby Leedham 62
Robyn Morgan 62
Holly Taylor 63
Scott Sabin 63
Daniel Orford 64
Hannah Brown 64
Christopher Hughes 65
Daniel Meredith 66
Jordan Madkins 66
Elizabeth Taylor 67
Lynn Harper 67
Jade Ross 68
Leann McCallum 68
Adam Bourne 69
Shanna Guest 69
Craig Hampton 70
Olivia Hammond 70
Amanda Rose 71
Matthew Meredith 71
Richard Bloomer 72
Darren Godwin 72
Jack D'Arcy 73
Kimberley Smith 73
Libby Turton 74

| | |
|---|---|
| Owen Reese | 74 |
| Amanda Tomkins | 75 |
| Craig Hingley | 76 |
| Elliott Skelding | 76 |
| Emma Layland | 77 |
| Jordan Pargeter Jones | 78 |
| Iain Geddes | 78 |
| Becky Farmer | 79 |
| Laura Ann Portman | 80 |
| Stephanie Wheeldon | 80 |
| Samantha Round | 81 |
| Darren Moore | 81 |
| Kirstie Taylor | 82 |
| Laura Banks | 82 |
| Jessica Greensall | 83 |
| Emma Wastall | 84 |
| Rebecca Hemmings | 85 |
| Alison Clarke | 85 |
| Simon Morris | 86 |
| Luke Redhead | 86 |
| Luke Harris | 87 |
| Sarah Cole | 87 |
| Lauren Ignjatovic | 88 |
| Kelly Harris | 88 |
| Carleigh Tromans | 89 |
| Reece Mason | 89 |
| Danielle Smith | 90 |
| Amy Johnson | 90 |
| Jemma Worsfold | 91 |
| Emma Sproston | 91 |
| Paul Godwin | 92 |
| Ben Henderson | 92 |
| Jody Brown | 93 |
| Adam Pilkington | 93 |
| Craig Beresford | 94 |
| Emma Whale | 95 |
| Sian Hooper | 95 |
| Lloyd Rose | 96 |

| | |
|---|---|
| Emma Weaver | 116 |
| Jane Clare Ferrari | 116 |
| Philip Sandy | 117 |
| Laura Wood | 118 |
| Thomas Davies | 118 |
| Lauren Howell | 119 |

**The Giffard Catholic School, Wolverhampton**

| | |
|---|---|
| Kirsten Wells | 119 |
| Matthew Guy | 120 |
| Pariss Sailsman | 120 |
| Dominic Flynn | 121 |
| Jewade Graham | 121 |
| Dermot Kennedy | 122 |
| Laura McCaffery | 122 |
| Paris Clark-Roden | 123 |
| Kurtis Shinner | 124 |
| Ciaran Treanor | 124 |
| Laura Finazzo | 125 |
| Ashley Rowe | 125 |
| Nasrine Hermiz | 126 |
| Sinead Treanor | 127 |
| Jennifer McCarthy | 128 |

**Withymoor CP School, Brierley Hill**

| | |
|---|---|
| Laura J Babbs | 129 |
| Lynsey Harris | 129 |
| Lauren Flavell | 130 |
| Rachel Thompson | 130 |
| Ben Hough | 131 |
| Jason Bryan | 131 |
| Philip Batham | 132 |
| Hayley Davies | 132 |
| Lara Venables | 133 |
| ✳Joe Miles | 134 ✳ |
| Terri-Anne Powell | 134 |
| Louise Wood | 134 |
| Rhiannon Wood | 135 |

# The Poems

## THERE HE LAY STILL AS FROST

There he lay still as frost,
In the darkest woodland.
There he lay still as frost,
Not knowing where he is.
There he lay still as frost,
While we watch him all through the night.
There he lay still as frost,
While we watch him all through the night.
There he lay still as frost,
While the world goes by in war.
There he lay still as frost,
While the world knows not how to die.
There he lay still as frost,
When he can teach us how.

*Skye Andrews (10)*


## MY PARENTS

My parents are lazy,
They order me about,
My parents are crazy,
They always scream and shout.

I go to bed before seven,
I don't think that's fair.
My mom goes to work at eleven,
I think I'm going to tear out my hair.

My dad's cooking is disgusting,
My mom's isn't bad.
They're never trusting,
And that's my mom and dad.

*Sarah Smith (9)*
*Cotwall End Primary School*

## SCHOOL ASSEMBLY

'Alright everyone let's get going,
Get away from the window Bobby!
It's only *bloomin'* snowing.

Jamie, turn off that football match,
It's getting a total bore,'
'Oh please not yet, Miss
I want to know the score.'

'Be quiet everyone!
Or you'll have to stay in.
Johnny, get back in line,'
'But Miss, I'm only throwing this in the bin.'

'Okay everyone in we go,
Billy, stop pushing!
And Sarah don't be so slow.

'Good morning everyone,'
'Good morning Miss Polly,'
'Lucy is it Christmas yet?
So what are you doing with that holly?

Okay everyone let's try and be kind,'
'Miss Dixon can you shut that curtain?
I think I'm going blind.'

'Everyone be quiet!
You're giving me a headache,
You'll have to stay in,
Just shut up for goodness sake!

I think I give up,
Today's assembly is off
I'm sure your all happy now
I've even got a bad cough.'

*Yeeeeeaaaaahhh!*

**James Willis (10)**
**Cotwall End Primary School**


## THE LIFE OF BEETHOVEN

Beethoven lived, breathed and died.
He developed pneumonia in a cold, damp
motel room.
But why did he die?
I still want to know why he died.

He loved his music,
So why did he die?
He got steadily deaf,
Beethoven made his will three days before he died.
But why did he die?
I still want to know why he died.

Although he was known as an irate old fool
by his mother.
Beethoven's genius, his cleverness,
Was wildly recognised.

His funeral procession was 1000 at least,
Because he was loved, loved praised worshipped,
But he was still known as an irate old fool.

**Lauren Chaplin (9)**
**Cotwall End Primary School**

## DREADED DENTISTS

When I jump up in the morning
I don't want to leave my bed,
I've only just stopped yawning,
And I've got a pain in my head.

My appointment's at 3.30,
I forgot to clean my teeth.
He'll say they're still dirty,
He'll make me clean underneath.

My mom opens the car door,
I hear the drills drilling.
I can't take the pressure anymore,
I may need a filling.

I'm going to meet my doom,
I can't sit still on my bum.
I walk into the dentist's room,
And I've got butterflies in my tum.

I can't live my awful life anymore.

*Oliver Monk  (9)*
*Cotwall End Primary School*


## SCHOOL

S  is for science, which is great fun,
C  is for comprehension, which I dislike,
H  is for history, which is interesting,
O  is for Oscar Orange who lives in Letterland,
O  is for Ofsted which all teachers dread,
L  is for literacy, which I love best.

*Elisabeth Cox  (9)*
*Cotwall End Primary School*

## MY TEACHER IS AN ALIEN

My teacher is an alien,
She comes from outer space.
She's really silly and very ace.

My maths and my English,
Geography and history too.
I try to do my best,
And do what I have to do.

With her small electronic blackboard,
And her tiny golden chalk,
She messes Mike Davies about,
And makes him look like a dork.

Her lessons are brill,
They have a licence to thrill.
I love my teacher,
Even though she's a strange creature.

*Sophie Elwell  (10)*
*Cotwall End Primary School*


## BROTHERS

B  rothers are nice and sometimes a pain,
R  unning all over the place and messing up my game.
O  utside and inside I don't know what he'll do,
T  hen asks me to play with him too.
H  e's just like a monkey jumping up and down,
E  ndless fun we have when he's acting like a clown.
R  acing up and down again he really is a pain!
S  illy tricks he plays on me but I always get the blame.

*Laura-Rose Potts  (10)*
*Cotwall End Primary School*

## FOOTBALL CRAZY

My name is John Mcarty,
I play for my school team.
I want to play for Scotland,
Well that's my football dream.

Playing for Glasgow Rangers,
Running down the wing.
Scoring all day and night,
Getting the crowd to cheer and sing.

We played a match on Wednesday,
None of the team scored.
The final whistle went,
Then the away fans roared.

I love to play a game of football,
Playing with my friends,
I'm going to a football match,
But not till this game ends.

I like to play football,
I'll struggle but carry on the game,
I will not quit playing football,
Otherwise life won't be the same.

*Benjamin Cooke (10)*
*Cotwall End Primary School*


## SCHOOL HOMEWORK

School homework is boring,
It's really a chore.
I go to school next morning,
and hope there's no more.

I really, really hate it,
It's simply the worst.
When I've finally finished it,
My head's ready to burst.

*Elizabeth Abbotts (8)*
*Cotwall End Primary School*


## THE SCHOOL HALL

'Class line up now
Tommy stop talking
Leave Sarah alone, Colin
Don't run you should be walking.

Sit down class
Colin, get back in line
Right that's nice
That's just fine.'

'Good morning everyone,'
'Good morning Mr Rose
Our Father who art in Heaven.'
'Jamie, don't pick your nose!'

'Hallowed be thy name'
'Colin, stop stalking!'
'Thy Kingdom come'
'Colin, start walking!'

The class are glad it's over
Colin is going to tell -
Doing boring geography
Thank goodness that's the bell!

*Calum Jones (10)*
*Cotwall End Primary School*

## A Teacher's Life

The first day of term again,
I really don't want to go back,
I will try not to be a pain,
I don't want to get the sack.

New little polished shoes,
On children who mess about,
Classrooms clean and sparkling too,
I'm going to have to shout.
At infants who just can't sit still,
They really are a pain,
I really can't cope with children,
I wish it was hometime again!

I'm sitting in the classroom,
Beginning to yell and scream,
They don't seem to understand me,
They're just gazing in a dream.
It's time to go home now,
They're running down the drive,
I must go and mark the books,
I'll be here till half-past five!

*Harriet Barnfather (9)*
*Cotwall End Primary School*


## Space

S  ee the planets and the sparkling stars.
P  luto is extremely far away from Mars.
A  n asteroid strikes a faraway land.
C  omets look like they're shaking hands.
E  arth lies silent, still and peaceful.

*Ryan Evans (8)*
*Cotwall End Primary School*

## THE DENTIST

Today I'm going to the dentist,
I really dread the drill,
I might not be able to grin again,
Because I might have my teeth filled.

I'm sitting in the waiting room,
Reading a magazine,
I hope it's not my turn next,
I think I'm going to scream.

I really hate the dentist,
I hope I don't have to go back,
So I can go home,
To have a little snack.

*Jenny Bowater  (10)*
*Cotwall End Primary School*


## THE FLIGHT

High up in the misty sky,
Is where they fly.
A formation of planes,
Spitfires and Hawker Hurricanes.

They whiz around and curl,
Watch them whirl and twirl.
Some dive and climb,
Others glide from time to time.

They take off,
Land low.
When the sun rises,
They shine and glow.

*Michal Howship  (8)*
*Cotwall End Primary School*

## LITTLE SISTERS

Little sisters never get the blame
When they spoil a good game.

They take your favourite sweets
I'm a vegetarian so she eats meats.

She's scared of the dark so she keeps on the light,
So I tease her while she starts a fight.

She always hangs round the boys,
And wants to play with my toys.

She shows off when she's dressed,
She thinks she's the best.

Even though she is a pain,
I love her all the same.

*Rachel Lowe  (9)*
*Cotwall End Primary School*


## HENRY VIII

Henry VIII had six wives,
He executed two with shiny, sharp knives.
There were two baby girls, but he wanted a boy,
When Jane Seymour finally had one, it brought out his joy.
He married three Catherines, two Annes and one Jane,
Killing Anne Boleyn and Catherine Howard caused grief
throughout his reign.
Jane Seymour died in childbirth,
Then Henry didn't think life was worth,
Good riddance to Henry in 1547,
But he went down to Hell, not up into Heaven!

*Rhian Sangha  (10)*
*Cotwall End Primary School*

## My 2nd Guitar Lesson

I'm walking up his nice long drive,
What will I really do?
The last time I went,
I didn't have a clue.

I'm walking up his stairs,
'Alright Jake lad!'
What will I say, what will I say?
He looks kinda mad.

He asked, me
'Have ya been playin','
'Err, er' I mumbled,
Bet he thought I was prayin'.

'Well then, let's play,
If you brake a string,
Just say.'

'Show me . . .
E-major,'
*Beep!*
*'Oops,* that's my pager,'

'I played a bit,
I suppose?
I made up my own song that's it,
This is how it goes.'

He saw me beep my pager,
I plucked the top 'E' string,
*'Yeah'* I said,
'I really wish I could sing.'

***Jacob Russon (10)***
***Cotwall End Primary School***

## SCHOOL

I'm back at school,
I've got dreaded Henry,
As my class teacher.

He is strict and mean,
He has a really loud shout
Which goes down your ear.

History is next,
I've got Mister Jones,
He is even worse.

He is very old,
Miss T is his dreaded wife.
I really hate him.

Free time is after,
Known as playtime for us,
We play what we want.

PE is after,
Mister Nolan we have got,
I really like him.

He is a really cool dude,
He is a sporty teacher,
But works us hard.

Yes it's lunchtime,
I've got a ham sandwich
And some chocolate.

*Oliver Miles  (9)*
*Cotwall End Primary School*

## MY PARENTS

All my parents do,
Is yell, scream and shout.
I always seem to be in trouble,
Of that there is no doubt.

My mum does the yelling,
My dad he just agrees,
You won't get parents,
As mad as these.

My aunts and my uncles,
They are just as mad.
When I get older,
I hope that I'm not as bad.

I love my parents all the same,
Even though they are a pain!

*Emma Walker (10)*
*Cotwall End Primary School*

## DEATH

Death is the colour of blood.
Death smells like poison.
Death tastes like lava.
Death sounds like a volcano explosion.
Death feels like someone burning.
Death lives in a volcano.

*Steven Lawlor (9)*
*Cotwall End Primary School*

## THE DREADED DENTIST

I'm on my way to the dentist,
It's really cold outside,
I'll be put in a big chair,
And forced to open wide.

I'm sitting in the waiting room,
I'm dreading going in,
If I loose all my teeth,
I won't be able to grin.

I'm waiting outside the door,
I'm going to meet my doom,
He puts me in a big chair,
I look around the room.

I think he needs to strap me in,
I really am not willing,
For him to poke around my teeth,
Bad news, I need a filling!

*Lucy Smith (9)*
*Cotwall End Primary School*


## HOPE

Hope is crystal white angels.
It smells like an angel's heart.
It tastes like mountain air.
It sounds like goodness.
It feels like a perfect heart.
Hope lives in your soul.

*Jonathan O'Keeffe (9)*
*Cotwall End Primary School*

## THE UNICORN

On a faraway planet in starry space,
Lives a beautiful unicorn with a gleaming face,
Its sparkling horn is as white as snow,
Its face gives off a shining glow.
It roams around the planet all day,
Looking for somewhere for it to stay.
It passes waterfalls and flowing streams,
Through the sunlight and moonbeams.
Some have seen it but nobody knows,
The unicorn's secret just grows and grows.

*Nicola Floyd (8)*
*Cotwall End Primary School*


## THE HAZEL WOOD

Years ago in Hazel Wood,
The trees hooked together like a hood.
The nuts in the wood grew deliciously for the squirrels in the trees,
We loved the berries and the cherries to eat them for our tea.
It was a hazel wood,
A flower wood.
Many came to see the beautiful sight,
In the little old moonlight.

*Sarah Jayne Podlesak (8)*
*Cotwall End Primary School*

## WINTER

Winter is in the air that we breathe but it is not getting to me.
I will pretend it's summer again and ignore the bare trees.
Nobody will change the way I feel about winter's cold,
                                        draughty breeze.
Tonight I dream of the sun shining on my face,
Every day I settle my head and let my thoughts drift,
For I know that the dream will come again.

*Paige Loydon (9)*
*Cotwall End Primary School*


## WOLVES

W hen Wolves win I go mad,
O h no Albion scored how sad.
L et's chart a song to cheer them up,
V ictory will be ours with any luck,
E mblem scored and saved the day,
S o the Wolves have won way.

*Ben Ford (8)*
*Cotwall End Primary School*


## POEMS

P erfect things to read.
O h! I wonder where you get ideas?
E veryone should read them.
M y favourites are the humorous ones.
S o, what do you think about poems?

*Timothy Knowles (9)*
*Cotwall End Primary School*

## A TRAIN ON THE HORIZON (HAIKU)

On the horizon,
A train runs through the sunset,
Into the distance.

*Matthew Blackburn  (9)*
*Cotwall End Primary School*

## A DANGEROUS FLIGHT HAIKU

Aeroplanes burning,
Through the dark and misty skies,
I hope we don't crash!

*Michael Potts  (8)*
*Cotwall End Primary School*

## CHEETAHS HAIKU

On the boiling plains,
Cheetah cubs chase antelope,
In the heat of day.

*Matthew Richards  (8)*
*Cotwall End Primary School*

## MY PET FISH

I wanted a dog or a cat,
A hamster or even a rat.
But all I got for my treat,
Was a fish, not the sort you can eat.

I feed my fish every day,
I know he listens to all I say.
He swims from left to right,
But he can't tell us if he's alright.

Even though I love him very much,
I would like a pet that I can touch.
I still want a dog or a cat,
A hamster or even a rat.
But in the end,
My little fish had a friend.

*Zara Tong  (8)*
*Cotwall End Primary School*


## MY FURRY FRIEND

He eats from a dish,
He isn't a fish.
He has smooth fur,
He can't purr.
He can't slobber and pant,
He's bigger than an ant.
He's got a tail,
He's faster than a snail.
My furry friend can't neigh like a horse,
My furry friend is a hamster of course!

*Charlotte Malpass  (8)*
*Cotwall End Primary School*

# THE DAY I LOOKED UP

The day I looked up, was quite a day,
For when I looked up, the sky was grey,

'Is that grey sky? Can't be, no such thing,
I must just be imagining'
I rubbed my eyes and then I saw,
The sky was still grey, I'm not that sure,
I went inside and asked my mom,
'Mom, is that grey sky smoke from a bomb?'

'No it isn't, it's normally grey,'
'Oh I just remembered, it's always that way!'

*Thomas Sheldon (8)*
*Cotwall End Primary School*


# MY BIG TED

On my bed,
I have a big ted
We like to play in the shed.

We like to build dens,
And draw with felt-tip pens.

He wears a bow tie,
And winks with his eye.

I love my big ted,
And I cuddle him in my bed.

*Alice Davies (8)*
*Cotwall End Primary School*

## CHIPS

C  risps have much in common with these.
H  addock on the plate with peas.
I   rresistible, 'Hmmm' they certainly are.
P  otatoes are a must so far.
S  alt is sprinkled, if you wish.

Have you guessed my favourite dish?

*Alexander Harris  (9)*
*Cotwall End Primary School*


## ANIMALS IN DANGER

Tigers have claws on their paws.
Pandas are big and fluffy.
Elephants are huge and grey,
Those hunters will pay,
When the rhinos have *their* day.

*Sophie Freeman  (8)*
*Cotwall End Primary School*


## DEATH

Death is red like blood.
Death smells like poison.
Death tastes like lava burning.
Death sounds like a volcano exploding.
Death feels like a knife point.
Death lives *in a gun!*

*Matthew Clarke  (9)*
*Cotwall End Primary School*

## PEACE

Peace is the colour of a pink flamingo.
Peace smells like fresh clean air.
Peace tastes like my favourite sweets.
Peace sounds like a trickling waterfall.
Peace feels like a soft quilt.
Peace lives in a warm place
Peace lives in my heart.

*Sara Mason (10)*
*Cotwall End Primary School*


## HAPPY

Happy is like a yellow summer sun.
Happy smells like perfumed roses.
Happy tastes like trifle.
Happy sounds like a bright beautiful sunrise,
Happy feels soft and silky,
Happy fills up the hole in your heart.

*Rebecca Jackson (9)*
*Cotwall End Primary School*


## PEACE

Peace is like a white fluffy cloud
It smells like fresh flowers.
It tastes sweet like honey.
Peace sounds like violins playing softly.
It feels smooth like velvet.
Peace lives in the heart of a dove.

*Harriet Brough (9)*
*Cotwall End Primary School*

# HOPE

Hope is as yellow as a daffodil.
It smells of spring flowers.
It tastes like sweet wine.
Hope sings like a skylark,
Giving joy and peace.
It feels soft, smooth and warm.
Hope lives in an ever-flowing fountain.

*Matthew Guy (9)*
*Cotwall End Primary School*


# HOPE

Hope is red like a ruby ring.
It smells like perfume in the clear air.
Hope tastes like a chocolate bar.
It sounds like sweet music playing.
It feels like a soft cushion.
Hope lives in the heart of love.

*Oliver Deeley (10)*
*Cotwall End Primary School*


# HOPE

Hope is a golden coin.
It smells like the summer air.
Hope tastes like a lovely cooked dinner.
It sounds like a nervous breeze.
Hope feels like a soft-petalled flower.
Hope lives in a sky-blue land.

*Suzanne Nickl (9)*
*Cotwall End Primary School*

## LOVE

Love is rose-pink.
It smells like peaches.
Love tastes like strawberries and cream.
It sounds like birds singing on a hot summer's day.
It feels soft and warm.
Love lives in everyone.

*Laura Caswell (9)*
*Cotwall End Primary School*


## PEACE

Peace is white.
Peace smells like fresh bread.
Peace tastes like sweet chocolate.
Peace sounds like birds singing.
Peace feels like a warm blanket.
Peace lives in children's hearts.

*Carl Phillips (9)*
*Cotwall End Primary School*


## PEACE

Peace is blue like a colourful sky.
It smells like a fresh breeze.
It tastes like chocolate.
It sounds like a flute playing,
It feels like a teddy bear.
It lives in a field of poppies.

*Sarah Turner (9)*
*Cotwall End Primary School*

## HOPE

Hope is white like crystal.
It smells like freedom.
Hope tastes like air.
It sounds like wings fluttering in your face.
It feels like angels' wings.
Hope lives in your heart.

*Colin Oliver  (10)*
*Cotwall End Primary School*


## AUTUMN WIND

The autumn wind is damp and cold,
The leaves are turning spicy-gold.
Outside it's horrible and damp,
I go to put on my snowy lamp.

I'm wearin' my nightgown,
The people outside are giving a frown.
Smelling of autumn and living things,
Birds are flying with feathery wings.

When it starts to rain,
I get a big headache pain.
The rain is like a swimming pool.

The leaves are going purple and green,
I am keeping nice and clean.
The wind is rushing,
I am pushing.

I start to freeze,
And I put in my peas,
And start to warm up.

*Samantha Parkes  (10)*
*Gig Mill Primary School*

## MY STABLES

On my way to the stables, it takes a while,
Carefully climbing over the stile.
Heidi's drinking at the stream,
Visiting the stables is like a dream.
I begin to take Teasle in,
I take her breakfast from the food bin.
She nickers when she sees me,
And that will always please me.
I bury my face in her mane,
Even if I fell off her,
I'd love her all the same.
She'll always be there for me,
So I'll always be there for her.

*Bethan Hughes  (10)*
*Gig Mill Primary School*


## REMEMBER

Remember, remember the 11th of November,
The 11th day,
The 11th hour.

Two minutes silence for those who died,
Wear your poppy with pride.

Those who died in the war,
Lost their family forever more.

*Laura Godwin  (9)*
*Gig Mill Primary School*

## A NEW MILLENNIUM

New year is a time we celebrate,
The new year forth the old year gone.

We make resolutions to keep,
Like I won't keep picking my feet,
Or I'll clean my teeth.

This year was special does anyone know,
Yes! That's right, supposedly it was two
Thousand years ago,
The birth of Christ, the Son of God.

Yes! It was the millennium,
Now we are in the year 2000, a new century.
We all hope the world will be a better place
For all the people who aren't as fortunate
As us and live out on the street,
But we can help by giving money,
Even a couple of pence,
Every penny counts.

The money goes towards a charity that
Helps home all the people who live out
On the street.

So this millennium you could change
Someone's life, which would mean they're safe,
Dry and with a roof over their head.

So do what you can to give a chance to the
People on the street.

*Charlotte Rudge  (9)*
*Gig Mill Primary School*

## MILLENNIUM

The thrill starts in the middle of the night,
While everyone's holding their party-poppers tight.
Suddenly it's another year,
While the grown-ups are happily drinking their beer.
There's a loud blast as the music's turned on,
Let's dance, come on, come on!

Everyone quickly rushes outside,
As fireworks are shooting out really wide.
Rockets, screamers, and Catherine wheels,
Come on in everyone it's time for our meals.
Everyone eats the delicious feast,
Turkey, chicken, all kinds of meats.

This is something I'll never forget, I can't wait
till the next millennium, can you?

*Emma Stewart (10)*
*Gig Mill Primary School*


## MY TEA

It was a curious sight to see,
But when I came home to my tea,
My fish fingers started to jump around,
And one by one, fell on the ground!

*Danielle Emery (9)*
*Gig Mill Primary School*

# AT SCHOOL

At school
On the playground
Children were skipping
Boys the ball they were kicking
At school.

At school
When it was time for lunch
Everyone goes to have a munch
At school.

At school
As the children go to their rooms
'Get out your pens' the teacher booms
At school.

At school
When it's time for play once more
Without your friends it's a bore
At school.

At school
We hear the last bell of the day
We're going home hip hip hooray
At school.

*Kate Holtham (9)*
*Gig Mill Primary School*

## WHY?

Why doesn't Mars taste like Mars bars?
Why doesn't the moon taste like cheese?
Why doesn't the grass taste like rock?
And why not chocolate for trees?

Why aren't computers blue?
Why isn't the sky yellow?
Why isn't candyfloss black?
And why aren't the stars indigo?

Why don't owls come out in the day?
Why don't bats go boo?
Why don't cats chase dogs?
And why don't rabbits say shoo?

*Helen Irwin (10)*
*Gig Mill Primary School*


## THE DOLPHIN

Aqua-blue as it dips through the sea,
Squealing and jumping about with glee.
I want to jump in with it,
With the dolphin so very fit.
It splashes its tail and slaps its fins,
Over the water it splashes and skims.
I feed it tuna and I feed it fish,
It goes splash, splash, splosh and splish.
I put on my wet suit and I jump in,
Holding the pretty dolphin's fins,
We sail through the ocean deep,
It takes me back to land and gives a cry,
Then I say my last goodbye.

*Nicola Leiper (9)*
*Gig Mill Primary School*

# THE FOX MAN

The fox is good,
The fox is bright,
The fox always sees you in the night.

He sees you here,
He sees you there,
He sees you almost everywhere.

When you are asleep at night,
The fox comes out for a bite,
He searches from dusk till dawn,
Hoping he won't find a prawn.

When you are awake at school,
He is sat playing pool,
When he goes to sleep at night,
You wake up with such a fright!

*Melanie Jastrzebski  (10)*
*Hob Green Primary School*


# THE ALIEN

He is bigger than a T-rex
He is tough and strong
The alien has horrible green teeth
His hair is spiky and blue
Fat horns are sticking out of his head
One big eye is in the middle of his head
The alien has got big fat arms,
Two on each side.

*Alex Downing  (9)*
*Hob Green Primary School*

## SPRING

Daffodils, how gently they sway,
Brings back the memories of a warm spring day.

The sun on my face, the gentle breeze in my hair,
The sounds of spring are everywhere.

I recall the stream, where my aching feet soothed,
Channels of water, oh how they moved.

Transporting things from near and far,
Spring is new life wherever you are.

It soon will be gone to make way for a new season,
Goodbye to the spring, I know you have reason.

*Sarah Louise Jordan  (10)*
*Hob Green Primary School*


## PRETTY FLOWERS

I can smell summer flowers,
Growing in those long hours.
Every colour you can see,
It is very clear to me.

Pink, yellow and white,
These colours are very bright.
Leaves that shine at night,
Oh what a lovely sight.

Water flowers in the shade,
A pretty pattern we've made.
Time for me to rest,
After all I've done my best.

*Sarah Curtis  (11)*
*Hob Green Primary School*

## MY FAITHFUL FRIEND

My faithful friend,
Is always there,
With his big, wet nose,
And shaggy hair.

He sits by the fire,
And looks at me,
And wags his tail,
When he wants his tea.

We walk together,
From dusk till dawn,
In all kinds of weather,
Maybe even a storm.

My faithful friend,
Depends on me,
To keep him warm,
Provide his tea.

I love my friend,
And he loves me,
We work together,
In harmony.

*Laura Collins  (11)*
*Hob Green Primary School*

## I HAVE A DREAM

I have a dream that in the future we will be able to fly.
I have a dream that we will all die.
I have a dream that cars will hover.
I have a dream that we will all lie around and never bother.

I have a dream that we will evolve.
I have a dream that the moon will dissolve.
I have a dream that England will win gold medals.
I have a dream that bikes will go without pedals.

I have a dream of the next 1000 years.

*Adam Johnson  (11)*
*Hob Green Primary School*




## THE BLACK STALLION

He grazes under the blazing hot sun
Munching at his bale of hay,
Ignoring the world that passes behind him
Contentedly with a gentle neigh.

He holds his head up, full of pride
A stallion, so noble and proud,
Swishing his tail from side to side
Stamping his hooves but not too loud.

He gallops around at such a pace
His eyes sparkling with delight,
His mane flowing with elegance and grace
Softly swaying from left to right.

He looks up at the midnight sky
The day had come to an end,
His body weary, he closes his eyes
Sleep well black stallion, my friend.

*Cherelle Bashford  (11)*
*Hob Green Primary School*

## MY GARDEN

Once I lived in a house like this,
With flowers and trees that twist.
The flowers are red, the grass is green,
The flowers are purple with yellow and green.
Some stand tall and some stand small,
Enjoying the daylight sun.

*John Webb  (9)*
*Hob Green Primary School*


## FRANCE

F  is for France the country of romance,
R  is for rouge the colour of love,
A  is for angelic which all the girls are,
N  is for no worries they're all on me,
C  is for cuddles people are giving,
E  is for enemies that you'll never have.

*Rachael Perry  (11)*
*Hob Green Primary School*


## OLD LADY FROM LYE

There was an old lady from Lye
Who kept eating rich apple pie.
She got so tubby,
She divorced her hubby,
And thought to herself why, oh why?

*Nicholas Johnson  (10)*
*Hob Green Primary School*

## THE CAR MADE FROM SNOW

Jim and Jon and Ron and Jo,
Made a car complete with snow.
But just then to their surprise,
The car they made came alive!

The car wasn't happy it shouted and snapped,
His horn made from snow was constantly papped.
He was really grumpy, he huffed and groaned,
He sighed and tutted while he puffed and moaned.

They all jumped in and had a ride,
They sat in the back, side by side.
Then they kicked it down but it kept on talking,
And they ran off from it but it started walking.

*Then*

Crash, bang wallop whoosh the car went away,
But Jim and Jon and Ron and Jo still look for it today.
Up and down and high and low,
Where's their car made from snow?

***Kelly Davies  (11)***
***Hob Green Primary School***


## THE SUNSET

As the sun sets on the moonlit horizon,
Night slowly turns to day.
Suddenly it starts to rain,
Once the rain has stopped
The sky is filled with the beautiful colours of a rainbow.
As I gaze upon this scene of tranquillity,
I think how wonderful the world is.

***Emily Bills  (11)***
***Hob Green Primary School***

# THE ANIMALS SAID . . .

The ape said to the fish,
'I fancy a dish of oxtail soup for two!'
Said the fish to the ape,
'I'd much rather gape at a bouncing kangaroo!'

The cat said to the lion,
'I just love to iron the shirts on the kitchen floor!'
Said the lion to the cat,
'I sit on mats and am worshipped by people all day!'

The shark said to the squid,
'I've just lost the lid to my favourite pencil case!'
Said the squid to the shark,
'I sit in the dark and dream and dream all day!'

*Daniel Mead  (11)*
*Hob Green Primary School*

# MY FISH

I have a fish,
That lives in a dish,
It drives me mad,
Just like my dad,
It's rather fat,
Just like my cat,
He loves my mom Wendy,
As she is very trendy.

*Heather Maynes  (10)*
*Hob Green Primary School*

## My Family

I live with my family,
There's Mom, Dad and me.
I love my family,
They're the best there could be.

My mom is lovely,
I love her so much.
She gives me loads of cuddles
And tons of affection and fuss.

My dad is a chauffeur,
For the Mayor of Dudley.
He works day and night,
To provide things for me.

I have lots of pets, a dog called Bessie,
There's Jasmine and Ariel, Tommy and Sooty.
There's Spike and my three fish who swim around all day,
Bessie waits for me to come home and play.

A family whose love means so much to me,
My nan Hilda and grandad Jack idolise me.
I love Nan and Grandad they really are great,
When I go to visit them I love to stay late.

My family are special,
I love them so much.
We will always be close
And love each other very much.

*A family means love!*

**Heidy-Victoryia Cox (11)**
**Hob Green Primary School**

## ALL AT NIGHT

I'm sitting here alone in my room,
shivering like mad,
I feel like I'm in a tomb,
underground at night.
I have a little room,
so I quite often have a fright.
I hear talking from downstairs,
I have a dream about bears coming after me
and giving me a fright.
I see pitch-black nothingness,
I also hear the wind going swiftly
through my room,
I can't sleep . . .
I can't sleep . . .
I can't s l e e p.

*Christopher Whiting  (9)*
*Joseph Turner Primary School*


## NIGHT-TIME

Creepy crawlies in my bed
As I dream inside my head.
Fast asleep in my bed
As I hold my tweety bear.
I had my pyjamas on nice and warm
I can hear the trees tapping on the wall.
How do you s
        l
          e
           e
            p?

*Lucy Howes  (9)*
*Joseph Turner Primary School*

## WHAT'S THAT?

I hear dogs howling in the street,
An owl hooting on a branch,
Then everything goes silent.
Suddenly some people start talking,
But what scares me the most is the tap
Dripping in the bathroom.
Chains clanging as my dad locks the door,
I hear the TV being turned off,
Then I see some lights flashing through my curtains.
I get up and open them, but it's only a car.
I get back into my nice cosy bed.
I hear floorboards creaking,
A door squeaking,
But it's only my mom and dad
Coming to kiss me goodnight.

*Samantha Hixon (9)*
*Joseph Turner Primary School*


## TUESDAY NIGHT

It is dark on a Tuesday.
Everybody's in bed.
But not me -
I can't rest my head.
My mom said
'Go to sleep, it is late.'
'No Mom, it's only half-past eight.'
My dad came in and put me to bed.
He told me a story,
I can't get it out of my head.
The moon is shining, shining at me.
It is soon night again, look and you will see.

*Laura Paskin (8)*
*Joseph Turner Primary School*

## AT NIGHT

At night I can see
Sparkling stars,
A full moon.
I can hear
Taps dripping into a bowl,
Dogs barking
From next door's back yard,
Winds whistling
Through the night.
At night I can see
Pitch-black clouds in the sky.
I can hear
Owls hooting.
At night I have
Scary dreams,
I think they will last forever.
At night I can see
Lights going on and off.
I can hear
Trees tapping on the window,
And then I go to sleep, sleep, sleep!

*Gemma Perry  (9)*
*Joseph Turner Primary School*


## DEAR WORLD

When the Earth was young
Life was sweet.
Speckled butterflies danced
In the golden sun.
Rivers laughed and bubbled
As they tumbled down the mountainside.

But now the Earth has
Changed into a massive disaster.
Disgusting factories vomit
Oil and filth
Into grassy cornfields
And pollute the seas.
People throw garbage
And trash the planet.

*Ross Allmark  (10)*
*Joseph Turner Primary School*


## AT NIGHT

Here I lie in bed.
It's foggy and misty.
Outside I can hear
The creaks of stairs,
The slamming of car doors,
There are shadows on the wall,
It's gone all silent.
Mom and Dad have gone to bed,
Little drips are coming from the tap.
I like it in my bed,
It's warm and peaceful.
Out there, up in the sky
Is a moon and thousands of stars.
The baby is quietly sleeping,
The lights are reflecting on my curtains,
The trees are swaying to and fro,
The cats are fighting in the street,
Suddenly I just drift into a deep sleep.

*Amiee Thomas  (8)*
*Joseph Turner Primary School*

## WHAT'S THAT NOISE?

Creeping slowly as I was going to bed,
I had a little thought in my head.
What happened in the night?
I wondered if it would give me a fright?
Slowly listening to what was to be heard,
What would it be? Whistle, whistle,
It might be a bird!
It could be a dog!
Or even a frog!
*Creak, creak*, what could it be?
I hope I fall asleep 'cause I don't want to see!
*Clatter, clatter*, I wish it was light,
Because it's starting to give me a fright!
*Splash, splash*, what could it be?
Oh please, will someone tell me?
*Click!* That's better, now the light's on,
Now I can see what's going on.
The creaks were only my mom
And the clatter was only my drum
Which was a tom-tom.
The splashes were only the bathroom tap,
Now, that's that!

*Chelsea Roper  (8)*
*Joseph Turner Primary School*


## DEAR WORLD

When the world was an infant,
The stars came round and said
Your name is Earth Junior after your father,
Then the moon came down and said
You will start a new life with planets and creatures.
The sun will set at 7 o'clock that's the time
You will close your eyes and go to sleep,
And let the world have its peace.

The morning comes and the birds will sing.
The butterflies will dance
The flowers will sway
As the blossom trees open the way.
The grass is sweet for the rabbits to eat,
The ducks swim as the birds fly high in the sky.
The Earth is getting older
And the world is getting rough,
But the birds are still flying in the midnight misty dusk.

*Jordan Evans (10)*
*Joseph Turner Primary School*


## DEAR WORLD

When the world was an infant
There were fields of gorgeous blooming daffodils.
The days were as sweet as red roses.
The trees were crammed with cherries.
Life was great.
The fish swam in great crowds,
In the water,
Laughing and giggling.
The birds nested in trees,
And sang sweetly.
But now the world has changed.
There are garbage and rubbish dumps.
People catch the fish and kill them for food.
The world was great but now it's different.
I hate this world,
Rubbish everywhere.
They pollute the sea, kill whales, fish and dolphins.
It's terrible.
They kill elephants for tusks.
I really do not like this world.

*Gemma Jones (10)*
*Joseph Turner Primary School*

## THE EARTHQUAKE

Enormous cracks are opening up wide,
Screams of terror are cried,
People are trapped under rubble,
Citizens are dying,
The quake is still destroying . . . everything.

Buildings turning into crumpled ruins,
Nowhere to run
And nowhere to hide,
Hours upon hours of waiting,
In the cold people are suffering.

Still the earthquake rumbles on,
People are frightened,
They're giving up,
Too scared to move,
Danger is all around.

*Rebecca Jeavons  (11)*
*Joseph Turner Primary School*

## BEDTIME

There I lie looking up at the sky,
I see the stars twinkling in my eyes,
Shadows walk across the wall,
I hear dogs barking and owls hooting,
The wind whistling,
Mom talking,
Now I've got to go to sleep,
Goodnight.

*Laura Powell  (8)*
*Joseph Turner Primary School*

## DEAR WORLD

When the world was born,
And the seas were formed,
No human trod the Earth.
God made the grass, the plants, the trees,
The cherry trees that grew so high,
Blossomed beautifully in the bright, blue sky.
The long green grass swayed in the wind,
The animals, the plants and all the peace
Has been reborn into a new world,
A world where it's good versus bad.
Forests have been chopped down from their weak roots,
Factories letting out venomous pollution to the world,
People killing the joy of the world for fun,
They spoil animal lives for things they don't really need.
The rivers no longer have fish or clean water.
Now that humans rule the Earth,
The peace is now extinct.

*Mark Roper (10)*
*Joseph Turner Primary School*


## NIGHT-TIME

When I'm lying in bed
I can hear
Dogs barking
Cats fighting
Someone shouting.
I've tried counting sheep
I just can't sleep . . .
sleep . . .
sleep.

*Darren Jones (9)*
*Joseph Turner Primary School*

## DEAR WORLD

Before humans walked the Earth
Before they laid and dug up turf
The peaceful cherry trees blossomed with flowers
When the calm waters did not stir
Gorgeous fields of bluebells swayed in the breeze
But now water rushes frantically past
Bluebells live no more
The cherry trees have been cut down.

But now the world's grown old and ugly so it seems.
Now mankind has become litter bugs.
Rivers blocked with filth and sewage.
Even teenagers have become vandals to the community.
Graffiti on the walls.
Water isn't the only thing in the canal,
There is rubbish, dead minnow fish and sometimes
                                    shopping trolleys.
There are poachers, murderers and thieves.
I would rather live in the past.

*Zoe Williams  (10)*
*Joseph Turner Primary School*


## NIGHT

Silverly, silverly, over the trees,
The moon is drifting along the trees.
This window is getting on my nerves,
I would like to shut it.
It is getting very spooky in here,
I think there is a ghost,
*Ghost! Ghost! Ghost!*

*Adam Jones  (9)*
*Joseph Turner Primary School*

## DEAR WORLD

When the world was young before humans came
The land was full of beautiful daffodils
The trees blossomed, crammed with cherries
Life was good.

The land was as sweet as red roses
The green grass swayed in the breeze
It was a peaceful time.

The birds sang sweetly
But now everything has changed
The world has grown older
Deadly poisonous chemicals leak
Graffiti on walls, litter on pavements.

Stupid people killing animals for fun
They are spoiling our world
Venomous fumes are murdering our world.

*Shaun Barratt (10)*
*Joseph Turner Primary School*


## NIGHTMARE

I'm getting ready to go to bed,
I've got a feeling in my head,
I walk up the creaky stairs,
Holding my teddy bears.
I'm up above the dining room,
Sleeping on my bunk bed.
I hear things inside my room,
I'm looking into the gloom,
But all it was, was all a dream.

*Daniel Morris (9)*
*Joseph Turner Primary School*

## THERE'S A STAR UNDER MY BED

There's a star under my bed,
It's glittering and twinkling,
It's as bright as a light,
It's as soft as a cloud,
I just can't get to sleep
Because it's so bright in the night.
It's shuffling and ruffling,
I might call it starbright.
I can't catch it
But I'll be sad tomorrow
Because it will be time
To let it go back to its friends.
I'm going to bed now
          *Goodnight!*

*Charlotte Powell  (8)*
*Joseph Turner Primary School*

## SWEET DREAMS

Through the window at night
I thank God for all the wonderful things
in the world.

I can feel it
I can feel God doing the things
He is doing.

Now please put me to sleep
and I want to have
sweet dreams.

*Jamie Simner  (8)*
*Joseph Turner Primary School*

## GOING FISHING

I'm going for a little fish
Gonna catch a tasty dish,
Putting together my fishing rod
Gonna catch a tasty cod.
Fishing in a lovely park
Gonna catch a scrumptious carp,
Fishing in the sea so blue
Gonna catch a cold . . . *aitchoo!*
Hired this boat for thirty quid
Gonna catch a scrumptious squid,
Started fishing when just a tyke
Gonna catch a delicious pike.
Oh, the water ain't half dark
Gonna catch a tasty shark.

Here I am, a lovely carp
Swimming in the polluted park,
Here I am, a lovely pike
Trapped beneath this sunken bike.
Here I am, the lovely cod
Escaping catchers against the odds,
Here I am, a deadly shark
With all this oil it's getting dark.
Here I am, the lovely squid
Someone should stop this fishing kid,
If this young human continues to fish
We'll all end up a tasty dish.
So please help us; please stop him!

*Daniel Whiting  (10)*
*Joseph Turner Primary School*

# THE LITTER-PICKER

Without any sound,
I view around
The filthy, dirty, big playground.
The ground is covered with loads of litter
And a half-eaten salmon fritter,
Crisp wrappers, sweets and chewing gum
And chocolate shapes that taste like rum.

Ray dropped some litter and then he went,
This is called polluting the environment.
My friends and I are litter-pickers
And the mess that's made just makes us sicker
Than anything else in the whole wide world
Because it's destroying our beautiful world.

But don't deny it! You do it as well,
I do it sometimes, but please don't tell.
Broken biscuits and banana skins,
Baked bean tins that belong in bins,
There's loads of dirty, used-up tissue
And ripped up magazine issues.
That's what it's like each and every day,
I won't give up, I'll have my say:

Never, never pollute anywhere,
Cos for other people it's just not fair.
Keep the world in great health,
Then it will be full of untold wealth.

*Lianne Williams  (11)*
*Joseph Turner Primary School*

## AIR POLLUTION

People smoke,
They hurt themselves,
They damage the air
And each other.
Factories make pollution,
People make pollution,
All of us are polluters.
Eventually there wont' be any clean air,
Eventually there won't be any life on Earth,
*Stop polluting the air,*
It's damaging the environment,
Air pollution,
Please stop!

***Jacob Osborne  (11)***
***Joseph Turner Primary School***


## LITTLE BIRD

Lying on the riverbed
Little duck now you're dead,
You'll be there for many years,
Your mom will shed many tears.

Mud is all around your head,
Little bird now you're dead,
Wire is wrapped around your beak,
Nobody will hear you squeak.

Everything kills your water,
It's like you're going to the slaughter,
Your body is covered in oil,
Your water now is vile.

***Mathew Jarvis  (10)***
***Joseph Turner Primary School***

## DEAR WORLD

When the Earth was just a young infant,
Stars gathered round it
And told that it would have lots of many wonderful years to come.
All its fields were covered in deep red roses,
Trees bloomed with sweet cherries and apples,
Waterfalls trickled down mountains
And splashed down into a stream of fish.
Morning has arrived and the birds greeted it with a song,
Butterflies danced around the beautiful trees.
After that day the world changed,
People had come to Earth and wrecked it.
There was graffiti everywhere.
The next morning trees had been cut down and factories had been built.
The beautiful world has gone, now it's too late to change it.

*Damian Withers  (10)*
*Joseph Turner Primary School*


## THE EARTH TREMBLES

A terrible tremble runs through the earth,
Shaking the city for all that it's worth,
Like a train running through the ground,
People frightened, rushing around,
Buildings scattered over the land,
People running, giving a helping hand,
Rescue workers digging, but taking care,
Every person saying a prayer
Devastation now in place,
Smiles wiped off everyone's face!

*Amy Wardley  (10)*
*Joseph Turner Primary School*

## DEAR WORLD

When the Earth was just a young infant
Stars gathered around it
And told it that it would have
Lots of wonderful years to come.
All its fields were covered with sweet cherries and apples,
Waterfalls trickled down mountains
And splashed down into a stream of fish.
Morning arrived and the birds greeted it with a song.
Butterflies danced round the beautiful trees.
After that day the world was wrecked.
There was graffiti everywhere.
Trees were cut down and factories had been built.
The beautiful world had gone
And it's too late to change it now.

*Laura Jones (10)*
*Joseph Turner Primary School*


## MILLENNIUM

M  ore cures for cancer
I   llnesses like meningitis too,
L  ove and peace everywhere,
L  iving in harmony with everyone,
E  nough food and money,
N  o one homeless,
N  o pets abandoned,
I   ll men and women will have places in hospital,
U  ndergrounds will have no disruptions,
M  oms and dads will both love their babies and not leave them.
　　My hopes for the next millennium.

*Emma Withey (10)*
*Joseph Turner Primary School*

## DEAR WORLD

When the world was an infant,
The stars came down and said
'Your name is Earth Junior after your father,'
Then the moon came out and said
'You will start a new life with plants
and beautiful creatures.
The sun will set at 7 o'clock
That's the time you will close your eyes and go to sleep
And let the world have its peace.'

The morning comes, the birds will sing,
And the butterflies will dance,
And the flowers will sway,
And the blossom trees open the way.
The grass is sweet for the rabbits to eat,
The ducks swim as the birds fly high in the sky.
The Earth is getting older,
The world is getting rough but the birds
Are still flying in the midnight misty sky.

*Tara Grice  (11)*
*Joseph Turner Primary School*


## DEAR WORLD

When the world was young, before humans came,
The land was full of beautiful daffodils.
The trees blossomed crammed with cherries,
Life was a treat.

The land was as sweet as red roses,
The green grass swayed in the breeze.
It was a sweet time,
The birds sang their peaceful song.

But now everything has changed,
The world has grown older.
Deadly poisonous chemicals leak around,
Graffiti on walls, litter on pavements.

Stupid people killing animals are spoiling our world.
Venomous fumes and pollution is killing our world.

*Jack Aldridge  (10)*
*Joseph Turner Primary School*


## DEAR WORLD

When the world was new,
Before humans were formed,
When the world was untrod,
Large fields full of daffodils swayed in the calm breeze,
The days passed, as sweet as red roses,
The blossomed trees, spread with cherries,
I wish you were here,
Time has passed,
I can't believe what we have done,
You only sometimes see the sun,
I bet the pollution is on top,
All you see is acid raindrops,
Killing animals for food and fun,
What have they done?
Factories give out chemicals,
Smoke as black as midnight,
Garbage and trash on the ground,
Poisons in the sea, killing fish,
Graffiti on walls, saying nasty things,
Murderers killing innocent people,
The world is all dirty now,
Change the world, like it used to be.

*Jastinder Samra  (10)*
*Joseph Turner Primary School*

## DEAR WORLD

A garden of crammed roses,
Waved in the light,
The leaves were brown
And they floated in the night.

The daffodils fluttered,
The primroses white,
The cherries so red,
It was a fabulous sight.

The sun is smiling,
In a different way,
The moon is sleeping,
Every wondrous day.

                    Gone forever.

Trees cut down,
Factories spewing oil,
Smoke in the air,
Very polluted soil.

Trash in the water,
Deadly black oil,
People poaching,
Everything spoiled.

People cruel and mean,
Hunters hunting just for fun,
People building factories,
Killing in the dim sun.

*Lee Oakley (9) & Adam Scott (10)*
*Joseph Turner Primary School*

## DEAR WORLD

When the Earth was new, an infant,
There were fields of golden daffodils, sweet.
Life was great, before humans came.
Trees blossomed in the bright summer sun,
Butterflies danced, fluttered in the sun.
But no longer these things live on.
There are deadly poisons, polluting chemicals in our air,
People trash and spoil our world,
People get murdered, strangled,
The graffiti is terrible
All over the planet.
This world has changed a lot.

*Lucy Moore  (9)*
*Joseph Turner Primary School*


## DEAR WORLD

When the Earth was new, an infant,
There were fields of golden daffodils sweet.
Life was great
Before humans came.
Trees blossomed in the bright summer sun,
Butterflies danced and fluttered,
But no longer these things live on.
There are deadly, poisonous, polluting chemicals in our air.
People trash and spoil our world.
People get murdered and strangled.
The graffiti is terrible all over the world.
This world has changed a lot.

*Jade Thistlethwaite  (9)*
*Joseph Turner Primary School*

## WE ARE NOT ALONE

I think I'm very lucky
I am not alone
I have a loving family
I have a cosy home

Some are not so lucky
They live a lonely life
They may not have a husband
Children or a wife

One thing I am sure of
We are watched over from above
Our God up in Heaven
Gives everyone his love.

*Kelly Bowater (10)*
*King's Hill Primary School*

## A TIME OF LONELINESS

The day after the first world war,
The rich and poor,
Shed tears, tears that hurt,
Where bodies lay scattered,
Useless and tattered,
Flames from the fire,
Are slowly burning,
Brought by the air raid,
Now it's the time of loneliness.

*Emma Dolman (10)*
*King's Hill Primary School*

## MY FUTURE

In my future
Will there be flying cars
With chocolate bars?

In my future
Will there be silver dishes
With smelly fishes?

In my future
Will there be jumping carts
With magic darts?

In my future
Will there be little rocks
With ticking clocks?

*Abu Taher  (10)*
*King's Hill Primary School*




## BLUE

Blue is the colour of the sea
Blue is the colour of the sky
Blue is the colour of a beautiful ring
Blue is the colour of the bubbling spring
Blue is the colour of ice
Blue is the colour of the lit up globe
Blue is the colour of my mom's shawl on her bed.

*Jade Bristow  (9)*
*King's Hill Primary School*

# WHEN I GO TO BED AT NIGHT!

When I go to bed at night,
I see a shadow
Creeping on the wall,
It gives me a fright.

Is it Dracula
Looking for blood
Or is it a ghost
Wearing a hood?

No, it is my teddy in the light
Of the lamp,
Oh it is funny
When I go to bed at night!

*Dionne Phipps (9)*
*King's Hill Primary School*


# MY DAD

My dad is lazy, lazy as a bat.
He never goes away,
He never works all day,
He never does the shopping
My dad does no cooking because he is too lazy,
All he does is fix his car
And drink a cup of tea,
My dad cannot stop watching TV.
My dad is embarrassing!

*Christopher Perry (9)*
*King's Hill Primary School*

## THE PLACE

Why am I here?
    To feel magical and dreamy.
What can I see?
    I can see birds in the sky and floating golden leaves
                                  from the sky.
Why is this happening?
    Magical silken memories are being made for me.
What can I feel?
    Breeze going onto my face. It's wonderful.
What can I hear?
    Whistling wind, crunching crumbling leaves, floating
                                    on a boat.
What amazes me?
    Money on trees, gold and silken leaves.
What can I do?
    I can feel free and make wonderful wishes.

*Lewis Mason (8)*
*Mount Pleasant Primary School*


## WHY AM I HERE?

Why am I here?
The wind took me here in his hands
What can I see?
Beautiful exotic birds pecking grapes from the trees
Why is this happening?
To help me and make my dreams come true
What can I feel?
Smooth grass swaying underneath my hands.

*Thomas Houghton (8)*
*Mount Pleasant Primary School*

## NIGHT

Watch the children get into their beds.
The hedgehogs gleam in the glistening night.
The birds curl their feathery wings to sleep.
Listen to the adults snore their heads off.
Night comes slowly.
But goes away very quickly.
Watch the flowers as they slowly grow.
The grass goes greener as the summer arrives.
The nights get shorter and the days get longer.
It's holiday time.
The moon gets weaker
And the sun gets stronger.

*Abby Leedham (8)*
*Mount Pleasant Primary School*

## THE MAGIC BOX

I will put in the box
Four gold shining coins
That glow in the dark
A tulip-shaped diamond
That I found in the park
And the petal of a daffodil
I will put in the box
A photo of my family on holiday
And a present from my friend who came to stay
And all the love in my heart.

*Robyn Morgan (9)*
*Mount Pleasant Primary School*

## THE MAGIC BOX

I will put in my box
The comfy quilt of a nice warm bed,
The reddest rose as red as blood,
The fur of a snowy wolf.
I will put in my box
The first cry of a baby that will never fade away,
The colourful curl of a bird that flies in the sea,
The roaring sea that calms down.
I will put in my box
The first word of the queen,
The friendly voice of my best friend,
The shouting of the families.
My box is made of gold that shines like the sun,
It is in a dark old-fashioned way,
I love my box,
I shall swim in my box
In the wavy sea.
It crushes when I swim,
But sleeps in the hot sunny sun.

*Holly Taylor  (8)*
*Mount Pleasant Primary School*


## EGYPTIAN POEM

This is the mummy breaking the brick,
Smashing the stone only to find it six feet thick.
Up through the corridor finding paintings on the wall,
Running, running, hoping not to fall.
Searching, looking for a way out,
But all the mummy could do was scream and shout.

*Scott Sabin  (11)*
*Mount Pleasant Primary School*

## DREAM WORLD

Why am I here?
To explore the world.

What can I see?
I can see eagles in the sky.

What is happening?
I like to see the future.

What can I feel?
Wind flowing in my face.

What can I hear?
The sea.

What amazes me?
The money on the trees.

What can I do?
I can relax.

*Daniel Orford  (8)*
*Mount Pleasant Primary School*


## A MUMMY STEPPED OUT OF HIS TOMB

A mummy stepped out of his tomb,
And heard a sudden boom.
He jumped in the sky,
*Immensely* high,
And fell back down to his doom!

*Hannah Brown  (10)*
*Mount Pleasant Primary School*

## MY DREAM

Why am I here?
I am here in front of the blazing sun,
To have lots of fun,
To feel comfortable,
Magical and dreamy.

What can I see?
I see eagles flying at the speed of light,
I see the exciting fossils and dinosaur bones,
I see nature.

Why is this happening?
I want to see the future my way.

What can I hear?
I can hear the splashing, wavy sea and the whistling wind.

What amazes me?
It amazes me because money grows on trees,
No badness and golden, silken leaves.

What can I feel?
I feel the breezing fast wind,
Blowing, tumbling me away.

What can I do?
I want to be free, have brilliant wishes and fly.

***Christopher Hughes  (8)***
***Mount Pleasant Primary School***

## NIGHT

Silently rests the house.
The old fence still holds together.
There's a bird asleep in the tree but does not sing,
Or the football banging the wall.

Night. Silence stays.
Or the bird whistles,
And the tall tree blows,
While the bushes are still.

Green the grass,
And green the tree.
Green the bushes,
With a still house.

Night, still silent.
All sleeps silently,
And the twinkling stars
Turn everything gold.

*Daniel Meredith (9)*
*Mount Pleasant Primary School*


## MY FOREST

My forest smells of sweetness
Like the grass that's just been cut.
The trees are prickly,
The ground feels soft like a cloud in the sky.
Tu-whit, tu-whoo, I hear an owl,
Wooooo, I hear a wolf howling.
A speck of light,
And boy I'm alright!

*Jordan Madkins (8)*
*Mount Pleasant Primary School*

## THE MAGIC BOX

I will put in the box
A star from the dark skies at night
And water from a roaring river
And a roar from a tiger.
I will put in the box
The waves hitting on the rocks
On a windy day,
Being buried in the sand
And only able to wiggle my toes.
I will put in the box
A dark stormy night,
An owl hunting for prey
And the rain hitting on the window.
My box would be made of pine.
I would take my box to a sandy island,
Where the sun shines all day.

*Elizabeth Taylor (9)*
*Mount Pleasant Primary School*


## MUMMIES

There are Egyptian mummies
Some have big fat tummies
These mummies are tame
Some carry no blame
They live in tombs
Where there is no bombs
Please don't grieve, 'cause it's time to leave
This magnificent mummy poem.

*Lynn Harper (11)*
*Mount Pleasant Primary School*

## NIGHT

Silently sleeps the rainforest.
The toucan holds its screech.
The leopard holds its leap,
And the parrot goes to creep.

The howler monkey howls.
Silver the leaves.
The sloth stops crawling,
And the jaguar starts snoring.

All the animals sleep
Like the whistling wind,
But one plants grows,
The animals know there is danger.

Everything is silent.
The rain falls.
The rain forms puddles,
One animal cuddles.

*Jade Ross  (8)*
*Mount Pleasant Primary School*


## EGYPTIANS

E   is for Egyptians doing their jobs
G   is for gods there are so many
Y   is for yes wonderful things
P   is for pyramids and I love to climb them
T   is for temples where our gods live
I   is for Imhotep who is one of our gods
A   is for Asines who is god of the dead
N   is for the Niles and I walk along them
S   is for Sakkara which is one of our town.

*Leann McCallum  (10)*
*Mount Pleasant Primary School*

## THE WINTER RAIN

The summer rain is soft, makes hardly any puddles
Autumn rain is gentle and makes everything shine
But spring rain is harder and makes things soggy
The only rain I like is the one that some people hate
The winter rain is the best but sadly it's all foggy
The winter rain is sparkly, and makes everything cold
Its icy reach makes icicles unfold
When rain turns to snow there's a silent eerie glow
And icicles drip of rain is like someone's tears
When lightning comes with rain it gives everybody fears
Some birds live on the water paddling round and round
Nobody knows what they might have found
And that's why I like the mystery of winter rain.

*Adam Bourne (9)*
*Mount Pleasant Primary School*


## THE WINTER SUN

The winter sun is
Twinkling and sinking
In a mischievous way.
It feels hard and soft
And moths hide from far and far away.
The winter I like best is the winter sun,
Because it comes gently before.
I come with my mum
And whistling, singing, forgetting a thing,
Glistening here, glistening there
While my mum stares.
So I know I'm happy in the winter sun.

*Shanna Guest (8)*
*Mount Pleasant Primary School*

## NIGHT

Silently sleeps the river.
In the dark dark park,
Wild animals do not run.
Silver the grass
Silver the trees.

Night. Quietness unfolds.
Only the murmurs,
And the glistening moon glows.
Turns everything to silver.

Silver the river,
Silver the trees.
Silver the grass,
Silver the pond.

Night. Quietness unfolds.
Everything sleeps,
And the night turns,
Nothing dares to move.

*Craig Hampton  (9)*
*Mount Pleasant Primary School*


## EGYPTIAN POEM

Down falls the cotton-wrapped faceless mummy,
No brain, no eyes, no heart, no tummy,
The mummy is colourful, ancient and old,
The magnificent mummy is covered in mould,
It's in the Sphinx, gloomy and dark,
Lies the mummy, cold and stark,
In the tomb, a pharaoh lies,
Now you can hear its moanful cries.

*Olivia Hammond  (10)*
*Mount Pleasant Primary School*

## NIGHT

Night. Stars twinkling.
Not a sound to be heard.
bare are the roads,
Lights dim.

Curtains drawn, windows closed.
Not a bark from a dog,
Not a whistle from a bird,
Silence is all that is heard.

Black as leather,
Black as coal,
Not a light,
Not a soul.

Night, stars twinkling,
Only faint snores to be heard,
Leaves crawl along the street,
Trees sway in the gloomy night.

*Amanda Rose (8)*
*Mount Pleasant Primary School*


## THE VALLEY OF KINGS

Down into the Valley of Kings,
There was an alley with Egyptian things,
Like a wonderful mummy,
Or the servant's dummy,
And of course the Pharaoh's death mask,
And the mummy's cast.

*Matthew Meredith (10)*
*Mount Pleasant Primary School*

## EGYPTIAN POEM

Egyptians are peaceful,
Egypt's a place of pleasure,
A place that you might enjoy,
Hunting, pot making and ploughing,
Pharaohs and queens are very pleased,
With the work that servants do,
Just doing their job,
Like any old servant,
Helping with pyramids,
Just as well as making them,
So you've been hunting
You've seen the pleasure,
And met Pharaohs and queens
*That's the end.*

**Richard Bloomer  (10)**
**Mount Pleasant Primary School**


## ANCIENT EGYPTIAN POEM

Egypt is a historical land,
Which is made of sand,
Looking for tombs
Where you find Tutenkhamun,
Archaeologists measure,
To get their hands on treasure,
The pyramids so tall,
They make houses look small,
But the mummies,
Have got no tummies.

**Darren Godwin  (10)**
**Mount Pleasant Primary School**

## NIGHT

Silent sleeps the animals,
The rivulets react quickly.
Only the owl's cry exists,
But now it's fading, fading until silence rules once more.

Night; everything stops.
Only the fields whisper.
Swishing grasses in the wind,
A silver moon rides across a billowing sky.

Silent sleeps the twisted trees,
Gnarled fingers stretching out to touch the stars.
Flitting bats dance in the moonlight,
A wild and crazy ballet in the breeze.

Night rules again,
Small creatures stir noiselessly in their nests,
Soft fur enfolding their bodies,
Night's silvery shades dust the world silently, softly.

*Jack D'Arcy  (9)*
*Mount Pleasant Primary School*

## THE HUNGRY MUMMY

There once was a ten year old mummy
Who had a rumble in his tummy,
He fell through a hole
And found a bowl,
Tasted fresh food and shouted 'Yummy!'

*Kimberley Smith  (11)*
*Mount Pleasant Primary School*

## THE MAGIC BOX

I will put in my box
The voice of the wind flowing
The feather of a peacock flowing
The hello of an angel.

I will put in my box
The soul of a mermaid crying
A cup, full of the ocean swaying
The egg of a fish falling

I will put in my box
The heart of a bird glistening in the sky
The note of a band high and low
The stare of an eagle looking for prey.

The colour of my box is a splashy blue
On the lid silver and gold stars
On the side the moon.

I will ride in my box
Past the beaches, past the fields of grass,
Into a foreign town.

*Libby Turton  (8)*
*Mount Pleasant Primary School*


## NIGHT

Silently in slumber are the trees of the rainforest.
The moon illuminating the jaguar's reflection in the river.
The monkey settling down in his favourite spot in the tree.
The trees rustle in the gentle breeze.

Night, so quiet.
The moon casts a spell on the sleeping river.
The leaves on the ground not daring to move.
The moon lights the trees like a casino.

The moon turns the creatures silver.
The trickling river not trickling.
The hopping frogs not hopping.
Stars like twinkling eyes in the sky.

Night, so quiet.
The parrot not squawking.
The dripping leaves not dripping.
The eyes of the jaguar closed.

*Owen Reese  (8)*
*Mount Pleasant Primary School*


## NIGHT

All the insects are sleeping
Catty, who lives next door, is snoring.
The grass doesn't move,
Nor the cricket jump.

Night, quiet comes.
Only the guinea pigs squeal and squeak
And the top of the shed shudders,
All the animals jump.

The cat jumps,
Insects get hassled.
Guinea pigs get jerky,
The grass sways.

Night, quiet comes.
The cricket doesn't jump.
All is quiet in the garden
And the top of the shed shudders.
Then all the animals jump!

*Amanda Tomkins  (8)*
*Mount Pleasant Primary School*

## THE SUMMER SUN

The summer sun
bright and shiny
the winter's sun deadly and bold
the autumn sun quite shivery and watery
the spring sun making it cold.
The sun I love the best
comes shiny and bright
glistening like the gold in the treasure chest
the sun is the best
because it shines like a shiny crest
up in the sky
like a jewel shining there.

*Craig Hingley  (8)*
*Mount Pleasant Primary School*


## VISIT EGYPT

Visit Egypt all, see a wonderful wall
Climb a pyramid, *but* don't fall
Float down the Nile, scare crocodiles
Visit a tomb of Tutenkhamun
Go to Pharaoh's land, and see lots of sand
So you've seen the land
Touched the sand
Been in a tomb, of Tutenkhamun
Saw the wall
And you have visited Egypt tall.

*Elliott Skelding  (11)*
*Mount Pleasant Primary School*

## MY MAGIC BOX OF SECRETS

In my box I have
The roar of my white dragon,
A pinch of sand from the hottest desert,
The voice of my mom's nagging,
The tail feather of a handsome pheasant.

In my box I have
An ancient scarab beetle,
The breath of panting cheetah,
A lion's first kill,
A beautiful blazing summer star.

In my box I have
The stillness of a winter night,
The smile of a newborn baby,
A beautiful pink and orange sunset,
The beak of a pure white dove.

In my box I have
A bright blue sky,
A mouldy chip off a Tudor house,
A glossy drop of blood from Anne Boleyn,
A fresh green leaf from the tip of a tree.

In my box I have
A big space
For memories to come.

*Emma Layland  (10)*
*Mount Pleasant Primary School*

## My Forest

In my forest I wander around,
I stumble and blunder.
I walk in the crunchy leaves.
The birds whistle a tune.
The branches are entwined and twisted.
I see a deer, it looks so smooth and joyful.
I wander further in, I feel happy, I see a silky stream,
I'm glad because I feel like something cool.
The smell is like wild flowers.
The tune is getting louder.
I feel like I could be there forever.
I can see light, I go so slowly and steadily towards it.
I get closer,
The squirrels are running up the tree,
I can hear the sound of the squirrels scrambling.
I get closer to the clearing,
I'm out, I brush myself down,
I still feel so happy to stay
But I go back *home!*

*Jordan Pargeter Jones  (8)*
*Mount Pleasant Primary School*


## My Secret Box

In my secret box I've placed
The glaring sirens of a police car on a busy street,
The dangling harness from a high brick wall,
The bronze capped bullets in a clear ice case.

In my box of secrets is
The dent in the wing of a fiery red car,
The sleek rubbery tyres of a roaring racing car,
Skydiving out of a whirling helicopter without a safety parachute.

In my box I will add
A disaster on holiday in the fifth season of the black sun,
The golden shimmering sand from the beach.

I will put into my box
The juice of a leaking red heart from a passionate girl.
I cannot open my box because the secrets will come back out!

*Iain Geddes  (9)*
*Mount Pleasant Primary School*


## IN MY BOX

In my box I'll put
A stone of hail on a summer's day,
A sparkle of sunshine when it's winter's way.

In my box I'll put
The first huge cheer,
Of the month in the year.

In my box I'll put
A moon in the day,
And a sun as I say.

In my box I'll put
A star that twinkles,
And an elephant with wrinkles.

In my box I'll put
Wonderland which I'll
Touch with my hand.

In my box I'll leave
An empty corner to put my memories in.

*Becky Farmer  (9)*
*Mount Pleasant Primary School*

## MY MAGNIFICENT BOX

I will put in my box
The day and night,
The stormy weather that crashes and bangs.

I will put in my box
The future light,
The golden sun, that glitters and runs, across the path.

I will put in my box
The love and sorrow,
The castle dungeons,
The knights of thunder, storming past the riverside.

I will put in my box
The waves of water,
The golden sand, that gleams in the sunlight.

*Laura Ann Portman  (9)*
*Mount Pleasant Primary School*


## IMAGINARY FORESTS

Crunchy leaves over the ground,
Crunch, crisp, crunch, crisp.
Silky, small, rubbery leaves still on the trees.
I can hear birds singing,
Tweet-tweet, tweet-tweet.
Damp grass, smooth foxes so smooth to touch.
What's that noise?
It's a silver, silky, smooth stream.
It is so beautiful in my imaginary forest.

*Stephanie Wheeldon  (7)*
*Mount Pleasant Primary School*

## MY SECRET BOX

In my secret box I'll put
A drop of juice from a pretty peach,
A mythical monster of permanent ooze,
A death on an African plain,
A dream of a ruthless Madame Butterfly.

In my box I'll put
A heart of love and passion,
A man with a black heart,
A cold pinch of bitter cold,
A very good impression on a baby girl,
A little bit of a poem with a little swirl.

On my box of secrets I'll put
An ancient mask of Tutankhamun,
A splat of blood from Catherine Howard,
And hinges of witches' toes.

In my box I'll put
My biggest secret
But now I'll shut its lid.

*Samantha Round  (10)*
*Mount Pleasant Primary School*


## EGYPT POEM

Egypt is a land of many wonders,
Full of spells and mysterious things,
Everywhere you go you will find mummies,
Including pharaohs with beautiful rings,
There are also pyramids high and low
Where Egyptians have died many years ago.

*Darren Moore  (11)*
*Mount Pleasant Primary School*

## THE FOREST

Prickly brown branches on top of a tall tree,
And flowers I will pick for you and me.
Flowers red, orange and yellow,
All different kinds of flowers.
I see a path in front of me.
A river I can see
With birds on a tree looking down at the rushing river.
I went a little bit further.
I went through some bendy trees
And I heard a quiet sound up in the tree.
I walked a little further,
It was a squirrel
Sitting on a crunchy leaf.
I saw a light
And I walked into it.
It is breezy,
I go home.

*Kirstie Taylor  (7)*
*Mount Pleasant Primary School*


## THE FOREST

I enter the forest, I smell beautiful flowers.
Oh, the leaves are crunching underfoot.
Oh, what is that noise?
It's the trickling of a little stream.
Oh the flowers smell wonderful.
I hear birds whistling, butterflies flutter about.
Then I leave the forest sadly.

*Laura Banks  (8)*
*Mount Pleasant Primary School*

## THE MAGIC BOX

In my magic box I will put
Moon dust that sparkles and shines,
A ray from the blazing hot sun,
Then some rock from Ancient Egypt.

In my magic box I will put
An icecube that never melts,
A tooth fairy wing,
Then a fish with no water.

In my magic box I will put
A shining star,
The rich crown,
A two metre sized house.

In my magic box I will put
The star of Judaism,
The Christian cross,
Then the Islam moon.

In my magic box I will put
A negative number,
Maybe a web house,
My wish to jump a mountain.

Now it's time to close the lid,
To keep my secrets in.

*Jessica Greensall  (10)*
*Mount Pleasant Primary School*

## THE SECRET BOX

In my secret box I will have
Special thoughts of Disneyland, Paris,
Hot summer days in the scorching heat,
Spooky stories to thrill and chill.

In my box of secrets I will have
Jokes of laughter that are very funny,
Not forgetting the Easter bunny,
Piles of gold that shine when it's sunny.

In my secret box I will have
Magical memories, mysterious moments,
Holiday hints glamorous and dazzling,
People sunbathing on the soft, smooth sand.

In my box of secrets I will have
Twinkling stars tiny and round,
But they have all fell right to the ground,
I'll have banging bands that make a loud sound.

In my secret box I will have
Fire-breathing fairies and dancing dragons,
Santa-shaped snowmen,
Diving dolphins, snappy sharks, funny fish, silent sea horses.

My box will be
Full of love and kindness too,
It will be open for me and you.

*Emma Wastall (9)*
*Mount Pleasant Primary School*

## MY ENCHANTED FOREST

I walked into an enchanted forest,
There were beautiful flowers everywhere.
I felt the touch of a sharp, shiny, spiky leaf.
I walked a little further and I heard a crunchy sound,
I trod on a heap of crunchy leaves.
I felt a tree, it felt like a rough cardboard box.
In the tree I found an owl in a dark, dark hole,
It was hooting.
I heard some birds singing a lovely, lovely tune.
Then I saw a speck of light,
I walked into it,
I was home.

*Rebecca Hemmings  (8)*
*Mount Pleasant Primary School*


## THE GOLDEN FOREST

In the smelly, spooky forest,
underfoot in the swampy, wet, gooey mud
I started thinking where I was.
There were four forests, one in front, one at the back
and one left and right and one out of sight of me.
For a minute I heard a noise, it sounded like a stream
and a bird singing on the branch, tweet, tweet, tweet.
Then I heard something, crunch, crunch, crunch. I
looked down and it was dead bones of old people.

*Alison Clarke  (7)*
*Mount Pleasant Primary School*

## MY SECRET BOX

In my secret box I have remembered the death of
Princess Diana.
I will put in the box a drift of dust and a mound of
wood left from the Mary Rose.

I will hear in the box Big Ben going ding-dong
all day long.
In my secret box I wish my dream would come true.
I will put in the box a white sun and a yellow moon.

I will put in the box the furriest porcupine and the
spikiest cat.
I will remember the time when Aston Villa beat
West Bromwich Albion 4-0.
I will put in the box a trap of sunshine.

*Simon Morris  (10)*
*Mount Pleasant Primary School*


## MY FOREST

It's a new year for the different coloured flowers,
Yellow, green, blue, purple, gold, silver, peach, apricot,
They all smell like perfume.
It's hot because the sun sizzles.
Rain patters on the petals.
When they die they scatter
Their leaves and seeds.
It takes a long time to grown again.
It's winter then spring.
They grow back again,
Now it's beautiful again.

*Luke Redhead  (7)*
*Mount Pleasant Primary School*

## MY BOX OF SECRETS

In my box of secrets
I'll put a mythical dragon
With rapid wings, a bird
Faster than the world
Could spin.

In my box of secrets
There will be a cloud with
A storm which will never end.

In my box of secrets
I will throw in a tiny pinch
Of fairy dust.
I'll place a model which
Nobody could ever see.
I will close my box
So that no more secrets
Get free!

*Luke Harris  (9)*
*Mount Pleasant Primary School*


## EGYPT

Egypt, a wonderful land.
Egypt, full of sand.
Egypt, an ancient place.
Egypt, a fantastic sight,
Go in a tomb, meet Tutankhamun.
Go, go to Egypt,
And see the bright sunshine.

*Sarah Cole  (10)*
*Mount Pleasant Primary School*

## MY MAGIC BOX

In my secret box I will put
A battered abseiling rope,
A canoe oar,
And a bow and arrow.

In my secret box I will put
A wish to go over Niagara Falls in a single canoe,
A wish to see my nan and grandad again,
A wish to see blue sea and golden sands.

In my secret box I will put
A tiny secret in the lid,
Which I have kept since I was a kid.

In my secret box I will put
A dream of horse riders in the dance room
And ballerinas in the stables.

*Lauren Ignjatovic  (10)*
*Mount Pleasant Primary School*


## EGYPT

Egypt, full of sand,
It is a fantastic land.
Go and see Tutankhamun,
Maybe some other tomb.
Go there for a holiday
Where you can relax all day,
Where your children can play
But please, please don't go away.

*Kelly Harris  (11)*
*Mount Pleasant Primary School*

## IN MY SECRET BOX

In my secret box I have
A bash on a head with a bell, chair and pew.
In my secret box I have
A machine to turn time back or forth with the
push of a button.
In my secret box I have
A speck of magic in the air.

On my box there is a window,
In the window
What do I see?
A bash on a head with a bell, chair and pew,
A machine to turn time back and forth with the
push of a button,
And the most amazing thing of all, the little
speck of magic in the air.

*Carleigh Tromans  (10)*
*Mount Pleasant Primary School*


## THE MUMMY

Many years ago in Egyptian times
in the land of pharaohs and kings,

When people died their bodies were kept
wrapped up in bandages and things,

Preserved in pyramids as they lay to rest,
this may seem strange and funny,

But today in history as we look back
we all know them as 'The Mummy'.

*Reece Mason  (11)*
*Mount Pleasant Primary School*

## NIGHT

Fountain, empty
leaves, still.
The bluebird does not fly,
the squirrel does not collect.

Night, darkness covers
only the owl hoots
and the wonderful stars
turning everything to stone.

Cold, the fountain
with its ripples.
Cold, the grass
of the cool, sharp steps.

Night, darkness covers
not a sound in the air
and the wonderful stars
turning everything to stone.

*Danielle Smith (8)*
*Mount Pleasant Primary School*

## ANCIENT EGYPT IS A MAGICAL LAND

Ancient Egypt is a magical land
Full of mystery beneath the sand,
From pyramids tall to the disturbing dead
Pharaoh's monument of his head,
Ancient Egypt is fantastic and grand.

*Amy Johnson (10)*
*Mount Pleasant Primary School*

## NIGHT

Silently sleep the fish
In a dark, black garden.
Wild animals do not scream
a single word or line.

Night, quiet enfolds,
only the owner murmurs,
and as the brilliant night turns,
nothing dares to move.

Snoring, the fish and the dogs,
Bold green grass on a pitch-black night
Night, quiet enfolds,
All sleep in nature,
And as the brilliant night turns,
Nothing dares to move.

*Jemma Worsfold (9)*
*Mount Pleasant Primary School*

## EGYPT IS A LAND OF MYSTERY

Egypt is a land of mystery,
The country with the most amazing history,
From mouldy mummies to the astounding afterlife,
Where the pharaoh remains with his wife,
The pyramids are ancient, huge and tall,
The gods are powerful, great and all,
If you visit this place you will see,
Egypt is a land of mystery.

*Emma Sproston (11)*
*Mount Pleasant Primary School*

## MY AMAZING DREAM

Why am I here?
The magic brought me here.

What can I see?
I can see bright shining gems.

Why is this happening?
I need to feel happy.

What can I feel?
I can feel green grass that is smooth.

What can I hear?
I can hear whistling wind in the air.

What amazes me?
The money trees amaze me.

What can I do?
I can be free.

*Paul Godwin  (9)*
*Mount Pleasant Primary School*


## THE ANCIENT LAND

This is the ancient land
That is totally covered in sand,
There are so many sights
And fabulous things,
You won't know where to start or end,
You can cruise down the Nile
On a luxury liner,
Or visit the mummy museum.

*Ben Henderson  (11)*
*Mount Pleasant Primary School*

## THE MAGICAL BOX

In my magic box I have
The greatest memories of the deep,
The best secrets you could keep.

In my box I've put
The best joys you could bring,
I have the bell rings and dings.

In my super box there is
The sea's waves splashing by,
I have the lions great green sigh.

In my box I have
The great light of the moon,
I have the month of June,
It will be the end soon.

*Jody Brown (10)*
*Mount Pleasant Primary School*

## DREAMLAND

Why am I here?
Is it because it is a dream?
Is it a thing?
Is it because it has to happen?
Is it happy, magical and exciting?

What can I see?
I can see giant mountains and shipwrecks
and ancient buildings.

*Adam Pilkington (8)*
*Mount Pleasant Primary School*

## DREAMLAND

Why am I here?
A magic giant bird grabbed me and
dropped me on a magical island.

What can I see?
I can see a beautiful white dove
sparkling in the air.
I can see a beautiful orchard.

Why is this happening?
I want to see the future,
I want to escape,
I feel happy.

What can I feel?
I feel the wind blowing through my hair
and my fingers.

What can I hear?
I can hear the sea smoothly, softly, gently coming
up by the beach and back out again.

What amazes me?
An island with multicoloured grass and sparkling leaves.

What can I do?
I can make wonderful wishes and I wish I could float.

*Craig Beresford  (8)*
*Mount Pleasant Primary School*

## THE MAGIC BOX

I will put in the box
the swish of the curtain in the wind,
boiling flames from the fire,
and the touching of your friends.

I will put in the box
butterflies that can't fly
you with wings,
magically gold.

I will put in the box
a bird walking strangely on the ground,
a feather flying in the air,
a bright sun in the sky.

The box is made of gold,
silver and diamonds,
stars and moons on the lid,
and your personality there.

*Emma Whale  (8)*
*Mount Pleasant Primary School*


## IN MY SECRET BOX

In my secret box I have a golden chain,
with specks of dust that looks like rain.
In my secret box I have a corner of dust
that looks like soot.
In my secret box I have an imagining
corner that is in despair.
In my secret box I have a memory
                    of my little nan,
who always used to cook her pancakes in a pan.

*Sian Hooper  (9)*
*Mount Pleasant Primary School*

## MY SECRET PLACE

In my box of secrets is
A speck of greyish moon dust
That glitters in the night.
I also keep the brightness of day,
It's placed into the right.
I have ten golden phoenix
Whose eyes shine in the sun.
You may also see lions in my box
While gazelles and cheetahs run.

In my box of secrets is
The worry of a knife
That would really hurt me.
My first day at school,
To finish the family tree.
When I fell off a gliding bike,
It hit my poor head hard,
I decided that I would wear
A helmet - no regard!

In my box of secrets is
The desire to surf upon
A rolling tidal wave.
To skateboard down the steepest slope,
A helmet would surely save
My head from being crushed outright.
I'd also like to stunt
With a Harley Davidson,
And a monster I'd like to hunt.

My box is made of silver,
And iron and gold too,
In it are set the finest gems,
But only very few.
On the lid are fairies,
Dancing, all aglow
And the hinges are of fingers,
As well as a single toe.

*Lloyd Rose  (9)*
*Mount Pleasant Primary School*


## IN MY SECRET BOX

In my box I will put
A trip to the home of cars,
And trips to countries where the golden sun blinds your eyes.

In my box I will put
A snow fight in the freezing cold ice of winter,
And the quickest speed ever, like cheetahs rushing
                                          to get their prey.

I would also like
A lit up pharaoh from ancient times,
And huge warriors from battles of old, with weapons
                                          red with blood.

Also I would like to add
A mythical giant stomping to and fro,
A picture of a spine-chilling ghost that thrills, chills and
                                          scares people half to death.

But now I trap the secrets in
Until the next time I open it again.

*Thomas Mullard  (10)*
*Mount Pleasant Primary School*

## IN MY SECRET BOX I'VE PLACED . . .

In my secret box I've placed
A wonder of words with silver shadows over it.
In my secret box I've placed
A rainbow that shone in the sky,
Then was gone like shock.
In my secret box I've placed
Eyes of a gold dragon on the hillside,
With red flames coming out of the
Nose of an Indian dragon.

*Lucy Hill  (10)*
*Mount Pleasant Primary School*


## THE MUMMY'S MAGNIFICENT MARVELLOUS LAYER

Every mummy has an empty tummy,
The land around them is extremely sunny.
All the mummies are asleep
And covered in a massive long sheet.
Dare you wake him when he's still?
If you do he'll come and kill!

*Shaun Dolphin  (11)*
*Mount Pleasant Primary School*


## THE SEA

The sea has lots of noises, with waves crashing against the rocks.
At other times the sea laps gently on the shore.
People go swimming in the cool water and may discover
dolphins swimming nearby.
The sea holds many surprises and hidden treasures, gold and silver,
but remember not to tell anyone, the sea holds many secrets.

*Grace Deakin  (9)*
*Old Park Primary School*

## NOISES

Noises in my *bedroom,*
Noises in my *bed,*
Noises in the *curtains,*
Noises in my *head.*

Can't sleep because of noises,
'You'll be alright'
My mother said,
But she doesn't know
What it's like,
To have noises in your head.

It's the noises in the curtains,
that I dislike the most,
Is it my imagination,
Or have I got a ghost?

*Whooooo.*

**Emma Baker (9)**
**Old Park Primary School**


## SCHOOL DINNERS

School dinners, yum, yum, yum,
Eating salad and a plum,
Some people don't like that,
They have lamb, well it tastes like a cat.
For desert you can have stew,
Some people hurry up and go to the loo,
Or you can have some fruit,
I can hear a flute,
Oh no! It's my flute class,
I need to go really fast.

**Chris Atherton & Mathew Caville (9)**
**Old Park Primary School**

## TEACHERS

Don't scrape chairs and don't be late,
Play with doors or swing the gate.
Don't make noises,
Don't drop food,
Whistling's silly,
Raspberries rude . . .
Never fiddle,
Please don't shout.
Never let your tongue poke out,
Don't lose pencils,
Bend books back,
Lose your plimsolls
(Or plastic Mac).
Use your hankie
(not your cuff),
never push and don't be rough,
Mind the infants,
be polite,
watch the grass
and never fight.
Keep off gardens,
don't pick flowers.
Read this poem
. . . but don't take hours!

*Janine Bosley (10)*
*Old Park Primary School*

## SCHOOL

I go to school every day,
To paint, to learn, to laugh and play,
My friends are nice, the teachers too,
We never run out of things to do.

On rainy days we can't go out,
We stay indoors, but can't scream or shout!
So playing outside is always the best,
But when playtime is over, we're glad of the rest!

Back in the classroom we do science, maths and art,
But maths is quite hard, so it helps if you're smart!
Just two years ago we couldn't do sums,
but now, thanks to school, we're as clever as our mums!

Before we know it it's the end of school year,
It's time for a break, 'cause summer is here.
We say 'Bye' to our friends and 'See you next term.'
But the six weeks go quickly and so it's back to school to learn!

*Kirsty Wootton (8)*
*Old Park Primary School*


## LORRY

A lorry came speeding down the road,
*Crash!* There goes his load,
Down the big green hill,
Because he didn't take his driving pill.

*Carra Powell (10)*
*Old Park Primary School*

## MY WORLD

My world is looking beautiful,
Baby flowers burst through,
Little lambs all skip and play,
Calves all leap and moo,
My world is looking beautiful
And we are beautiful too.

My world is looking beautiful,
Humans move and work,
Tiny babies born into the world,
How strange it looks at first,
My world is looking beautiful,
And we all sing and grow.
My world is really precious,
And we should keep it so.

But some people don't see the beauty,
In things that live and grow,
they make dirty cars and buildings,
And they don't seem to know.
The things that God has given us,
Are what I want to see,
The things that nature gave us,
Are what's beautiful to me.

*Abbie Louise Price  (8)*
*Old Park Primary School*

## GROWING UP

The boy next door is 8
And he lives at number 4,
In one year's time he will be nine
Because he's growing more.

The boy next door is 8,
And Tommy is his name,
Each day he grows a little more,
Although he looks the same.

Each person grows all day and night,
Although we cannot see,
Each spurt of growth is out of sight,
Or so it seems to be.

Each single person in the world,
Whatever age or sort,
Are seen to grow as people know,
From 1 to 1 nought nought.

*Gemma Southall  (11)*
*St Chad's RC Primary School, Dudley*


## THINGS I LIKE DOING

I was swimming in a pool
When my friend came out the house,
He had spotted swimming trunks
And a face just like a mouse.

I went out to play with a boy
We ended up playing tennis,
We were halfway through the second match
And I found out his name was Dennis.

*Daniel Watson  (11)*
*St Chad's RC Primary School, Dudley*

## MY CAT

'Mark! Go and feed the cat,
not too much or he'll get fat.
If he's fat he won't be able to catch the mouse,
which lives in our house.
If he can't catch the mouse
which lives in our house
He will eat all the cheese
and won't say please.
So not too much now Mark,
because we want him as quick as a spark.'

*Amanda Farmer (11)*
*St Chad's RC Primary School, Dudley*


## THE CAROUSEL

The horses - as still as flowers,
as quiet as sound.
Building up speed, faster than
light, faster than a hound.
Faster than Concorde, faster
than sound.
Slowing down, slower than a
tortoise, slower than a snail,
as silent as a flower.
The horses.

*Craig Cox (11)*
*St Chad's RC Primary School, Dudley*

## THE GODS

Zeus was the god of gods,
But he was rather odd;
His son Hercules was very strong,
But not as tall as old King Kong;
Atlas held the world in all,
His arms almost always sore;
While Hera's divine beauty,
Caused many sailors to mutiny;
The god of music - Apollo
Used to sing a solo,
But only after he had sucked a polo.
Aphrodite the goddess of love,
Can sing a song just like a dove.
Hades was the worst of the lot,
To dispose of him required a plot;
They joined together to devise a plan,
On how to make Hades a better man;
They gave him lessons and lectures alone,
But all he did was to groan and moan.
He'll never be a nicer chap,
So Zeus will give him an almighty zap!

*Alexander Fellows (11)*
*St Chad's RC Primary School, Dudley*

## SUNRISE

I'm in the summer meadow, the sunrise
is in the east while animals and flowers
wait for the feast. The feast of the sun,
the moon shattered in tears.
I wish I were the sun going up
every year.

*Rebekah Hartle (10)*
*St Chad's RC Primary School, Dudley*

## THE THING ABOUT PARENTS

The thing about parents is -
that they drive you round the bend.
They turn the telly off during programmes
You never see the end.

Then they yell and bawl 'Get up to bed,
you really need your sleep.'
Then in the mornings it's 'Get out of bed,
come on stop counting sheep.'

They're stingy with pocket money,
they pay half the minimum wage.
They never let you see your friends
It's like being in a cage.

At table they talk about boring things,
like work and their friend Sue.
Most nights it's difficult,
to stay awake all the way through.

They never let your friends round,
they drive you up the wall.
The thing about parents is
*You don't need them at all!*

***Eleanor Burns  (10)***
***St Chad's RC Primary School, Dudley***


## THE SEA

It crashes and splashes onto the rocks,
Like a lion pouncing on its prey.
It rips and it roars but nobody cares,
But when it gets angry it catches its prey unawares.
It reaches for sand upon the seashore,
And gives in return - nothing at all.

A hundred white horses upon blue silk,
Leaping and jumping over the fence of freedom.
A glittering topaz crystal maze
Looks after water animals with its gaze.
On a sunny day it likes to bathe in the sun,
It sparkles and glitters with all of its fun.
It always seems it's on the run.

*Rebecca Broom (10)*
*St Chad's RC Primary School, Dudley*


## SHOOTING STARS

Shooting stars
They're faster than cars
They're never getting slower.

Shooting stars
Don't stop at the bars
They're never getting slower

Shooting stars
Don't stop to buy their food at the Spars
They're never getting slower.

Shooting stars
Go ever so far
But still they're never getting slower.

Shooting stars
They look so bizarre
But still they're never getting slower.

Shooting stars
They're never getting slower.

*Michael Holden (11)*
*St Chad's RC Primary School, Dudley*

## SPRING

I walk through the garden
Beautiful flowers
Bright and beautiful
Birds twittering
Look! A beautiful glowing,
butterfly hovers around.
Fruit growing on trees,
apples, oranges
swaying in the breeze.
I sit down to pick a
sunny daffodil . . .
Which smells lovely
Springtime has arrived.
Eggs cracking
New chicks for Easter.

*Katie Rafferty (10)*
*St Chad's RC Primary School, Dudley*


## A POEM OF LOVE

Love is happy
Love is sad
Love can command
All that's bad.
It makes you glad
To be in love,
Love makes you
As happy as a dove.
Love never goes away
It will always be with you,
Wherever you go
And in your heart it will always stay.

*Siobhan Growcott (10)*
*St Chad's RC Primary School, Dudley*

## MY FAMILY

My mom is always moaning
My dad is always groaning,
My sister is always nagging
My dog's tail is always wagging.

My rabbits' bellies are always bloating
My fish are always floating.
My grandads are always raging
My grandmothers are always ageing.

My cousins always cheer me
My aunts and uncles are always near me.
My family is always there
My family will always care.

*Mitchell Riley  (11)*
*St Chad's RC Primary School, Dudley*


## THE DARK HOUSE

The wind was blowing
the trees were shuffling,
Just then I heard a cry,
a scream and a shout.
I turned to see what was there
I thought it was the air
I felt a breeze go down
my spine, someone told me
the house was mine.
I heard more shouting and
more screaming just then
I imagined a bowl of cream.
Was it a dream or was it a scream?

*Thomas Homer  (11)*
*St Chad's RC Primary School, Dudley*

# DRIFT ME AWAY

Drift me away to Heaven's golden gates
Where angels cascaded in silver robes await
All of my days I've been waiting
I closed my eyes and drifted away
I was lifted by my loved ones and taken as I lay.
I thought of the children - my son, my nephew,
my sister-in-law and sister too.
A familiar face smiled at me, dêja vu.
She opened her folding wings
And upon her head a heavenly golden ring
Then the most radiant lady arose
She smiled at me.
Couplets of roses lay around her feet
Her long blue robes folded in pleats
A large figure appeared, surrounded by light
He opened his hands
One hole in the left and one in the right.
Smiling, he took my hand and said
'I will take you to the *promised land.*'
There's no time to waste and together we
drifted through Heaven's golden gates.

*Jake Griffiths (11)*
*St Chad's RC Primary School, Dudley*

# HEAVEN

Sparkling fountains of ice-cream
White horses with shimmering wings
A colourful array of shining lights
And golden angels that sing

A giant feast of chocolate cake
A 100-metre waterslide
Never-ending stretches of beach
Where you float along with the tide

A football match that lasts forever
A hundred zillion half-times
Fruit-bearing trees for everyone
But no one chooses the limes!

Heaven's the best place in the universe
It has everything you like best
Like everlasting playtime
Love, peace and joyfulness.

*Anna Jones (11)*
*St Chad's RC Primary School, Dudley*


## IN THE HOUSE ALONE

Drip, drip, drip the tap has been left on
Trickle, trickle, trickle the bath is filling up
Splosh, splosh, splosh the bath is overflowing
Creak, creak, creak the floorboards are breaking
Crack, the floorboards give way
Splash, I'm soaked with water
Brrng, the doorbell rings
Aargh! Mom and dad are back
They don't look happy!

*Mary Clare Allen (10)*
*St Mary's RC Primary School, Brierley Hill*

## TICK TOCK

Tick, tock, tick, tock goes the clock.
Tick, tock, tick, tock goes the clock.
Ding, dong, ding, dong this is getting
Annoying now.
Oh, I wish I could get to sleep.

Drip, drop, drip, drop now it's the tap.
Drip, drop, drip, drop goes the tap.
Drip, drop, drip, drop this is getting
Annoying now.
Oh, I wish I could get to sleep.

Crackle, crackle goes the blazing fire.
Crackle, crackle goes the blazing fire.
Crackle, crackle now this is getting
Annoying.
Oh, good it's all stopped.
Now I can get to sleep.

*Ben Prime (10)*
*St Mary's RC Primary School, Brierley Hill*


## MY SCHOOL

When at school, I look so cool
When my sister's at school, she looks like a fool.
My teacher is Mr Swain
I think he's a pain
He think he's got a big brain
My teacher - Mr Swain.
My favourite work is art
My work is so smart
I can't wait to start my new piece of art.

*Natalie Bowen (10)*
*St Mary's RC Primary School, Brierley Hill*

## THE TOWEL

The lovely warm towel
    is waiting to be used
Along comes a person
    but never touches the towel.

The poor towel
    is very upset
It's ready to be used
    but no one cares!

The towel hears something
    then he realises that it's water running
He's very excited
    Oh boy, oh boy!

He waits and he waits
    as he gets hotter and hotter
Hark what's that noise?
    Still nobody comes!

Then he hears a thump
    something reaches for him
O yes, he had been
    put around a wet body

The thing made a sound
    it was a sound of an Arrrh!
Like it likes the towel

The towel is put back
    on the warm place
Where it was heated up
    the towel dries
It gets hotter
    Now I am happy.

*Heather Conroy (10)*
*St Mary's RC Primary School, Brierley Hill*

## A POEM ABOUT DOGS

Dogs are friends to us
They like to chase cats
Even though they're slobbery
They just love rats

One dog is my friend
His coat is shiny black
His name is Cujo
He is very, very slack

Cujo has white spots on his back
He tries to fly a kite
Even though he cannot do it
He tries with all his might

When Cujo is very cold
His nose goes really blue
And when he's on a farm
He just shouts 'Boo!'

When he's old and grey
He will lie down all day
I will shout 'Cujo!'
And he will not delay.

*Sorelle Sidaway (9)*
*St Mary's RC Primary School, Brierley Hill*

## RABBIT IN THE RUN

Rabbit in the run
Having so much fun
Likes to go in every day
Likes to jump and play.

Rabbit in the run
Lying in the sun
With juicy tender leaves
He's looking very pleased.

Rabbit in the run
Now the day is done
Time to go back to the hutch
I've enjoyed the day so very much.

*Hannah Shaw (10)*
*St Mary's RC Primary School, Brierley Hill*


## MY DOG SAMMY

His fur is grey and fluffy,
His eyes are really black.
He loves the program Buffy
The part where it attacks.

His bed is very red
But he wishes it was blue
And when I stroke his head
He runs into my shoe.

When he was gold
I told him he looked old.
I said I'll spray you grey,
And then he said 'OK!'

*Hannah Jamie (9) & Katty Clatworthy (10)*
*St Mary's RC Primary School, Brierley Hill*

## MY FAMILY

My mum's name is Pauline and she's great
That is - most of the time!
She is my very best mate
I wouldn't change her for a dime.

My dad's name is Richard and he's mad
Morning to night - he teases me
That makes me very sad,
Oh why can't he just let me be!

My brother's name is Daniel and he's football mad,
Football, football, football
He watches it and so does his dad
He just drives me up the wall.

So this is my family that I love dearly,
Even though they drive me mad
I mean it most sincerely
That's my mum, my brother and my dad.

*Emma Weaver (10)*
*St Mary's RC Primary School, Brierley Hill*

## FACES

My eyes are dark blue
My lips are light red
My hair is very blonde
With a little bit of red.

My walls are purple
My hamster's brown
I can't get to sleep
When he's running around

I like to eat chips
The one without bits
I like to drink cool coke
While having a soak.

*Jane Clare Ferrari  (9)*
*St Mary's RC Primary School, Brierley Hill*


## TEACHERS

There's a man called Mr Swain
Some think that he's a pain
He says he's a teacher
You'd think he's a preacher
Year 5 think he's insane.

There's a teacher called Mrs Moss
She likes to say she's the boss
We think it's the butler
That is Mrs Cutler
Oh, now we're all at a loss.

And there's Mrs Keegan Hobbs
How does she eat all those Hobnobs?
There's an element of gloom
When she walks in the room
With crumbs falling out of her gob.

And finally there's Miss Maher
After school she heads for the bar
It must be the kids
That are in year 6
That make her run for the bar.

*Philip Sandy  (10)*
*St Mary's RC Primary School, Brierley Hill*

## MY PETS

I have a dog called Barney
Who went barmy!
He kissed the cat
Who crawled into a hat.

I have a cat called Sukey
She went loopy!
She cleans the rabbit
Who had a bad habit.

I have a rabbit called Nutch
She lives in a hutch!
She has a friend called Butch.

I have a hamster called Fred
Who sleeps in my bed
He plays on the car wheel.

*Laura Wood  (9)*
*St Michael's CE Primary School, Wolverhampton*


## MAGIC SPELLS

Magic can be big
Magic can be small
With magic you never fall
Magic is great
But you never have it on a plate
Sitting by the fire grate
People staring
People talking
Because . . .
Magic can be big
Magic can be small.

*Thomas Davies  (9)*
*St Michael's CE Primary School, Wolverhampton*

## DRAGONS ARE!

Dragons are, dragons are
smooth, green and scaly.

Dragons eat, dragons eat
any human baby.

Dragons have, dragons have
long pointed teeth.

Dragons live, dragons live
in big caves.

Dragons like, dragons like
Dragons like to roam.

Dragons drink, dragons drink
Lots of red, red blood.

Dragons stamp loud and clear
So it reaches every ear.

*Lauren Howell  (9)*
*St Michael's CE Primary School, Wolverhampton*


## MY DAD

My dad is very tall - not very small.
He only has a bit of hair
But I don't think he minds.
He's always watching football on the telly
And his favourite dessert is ice-cream and jelly.
His favourite football team is Norwich
But he doesn't like porridge.
Sometimes he makes me mad
But I don't mind - because he's my dad!

*Kirsten Wells  (9)*
*The Giffard Catholic School, Wolverhampton*

## THE SEA

The gentle breeze rubs on the waves,
With storm no sign of showing
The waves whip and whisper in the wind
The sound starts growing.

The sound grows louder, storm breaks out,
The wind is growing free,
The wind wisps and whisks
Into the great open sea.

The boat lay wrecked and battered,
After the terrible clash.
The ship went straight into the rocks
The boat was destroyed in a flash.

*Matthew Guy (10)*
*The Giffard Catholic School, Wolverhampton*


## THE BONFIRE

The bonfire is now alight,
Fire, fire burning bright.
Mom, hold my hand real tight
Sparklers are sparkling,
Bangers are banging
Colours everywhere.
Appearing with their fierce glare.
Pop, pop, pop
They go whooshing into the air,
And light up the sky.
Then we say goodbye.

*Pariss Sailsman (8)*
*The Giffard Catholic School, Wolverhampton*

## THE DEEP, DARK, MURKY SEA

A kingdom for every creature,
The ruler, a king of great mystery
With the scars to show his history.
The horses racing to the beach
The white chariots behind.
Crushing objects in its path
With its powerful legs.
The sea is calm, throbbing left
to right.
Now it's drifting calmly
In this silent night.

*Dominic Flynn (10)*
*The Giffard Catholic School, Wolverhampton*

## THE SEA

I went to the boat to see . . .
The bright blue gleaming sea.
The fish looked grey
Swimming their different way.

I went to the island to see . . .
But an octopus looked at me.
I ran away, came back next day
To see what I could see.

*Jewade Graham (10)*
*The Giffard Catholic School, Wolverhampton*

## THE SEA

The mussels stuck to the rocks.
The crashing waves got bigger.
They were simply enormous
The foam bubbled furiously.

The black, seaweedy rocks
Were drowning in the white, whipping
Waves.

The lighthouse flashed, time and again
The waves were uncontrollable.
The cold sea was like horses
Galloping, fighting and lashing
Higher and higher.
The salty sea sprayed everywhere,
In the middle of the Atlantic Ocean.

The fish in the sea were thinking
As they were sinking.
In the cold salty, dark gloomy sea,
They then started to flee.
For the sea was carrying them
Somewhere where they had never been
Where they were going to die.

*Dermot Kennedy (10)*
*The Giffard Catholic School, Wolverhampton*


## DOLPHINS AND OTHERS

There they go, darting and whipping
this strong sea.
A ducking, diving dolphin as fast as the wind,
What a lovely life - messing around!

There're the cliffs hanging and watching,
Clashing and dashing, swallowing ships by
the whole,
The whipping, white waves waving at me,
Chasing after the run-away ships.
Howling and growling as he goes.

*Laura McCaffery (10)*
*The Giffard Catholic School, Wolverhampton*


## MY GODFATHER

I have a godfather whose name is Max
He's busy at work, he could sell you a fax.
He's brilliant at chess
But his hair is a mess.

You wouldn't want to meet him!

He eats too much curry,
Which is why he's so smelly,
And he spends too much time
In front of our telly.

You wouldn't want to meet him!

He thinks he's funny
And he'll tell you a joke,
Too bad he likes to drink and smoke.

You wouldn't want to meet him!

My godfather Max
Is skilful at sports,
But I'm sorry to say he looks chubby in shorts.

You really, really would *not* want to meet him!

*Paris Clark-Roden (9)*
*The Giffard Catholic School, Wolverhampton*

## WALLY WINKA ZOO

If you work at Wally Winka's Zoo
You'll find an awful lot to do
Six on the dot you begin to plot
The busy day ahead of you.

Fishes for the sealions, clap, clap, clap!
Mucking out the elephants,
Oh, my back!
Bananas for the monkeys swinging in the trees,
Washing the giraffes from their feet to their knees.

Ferocious lion cubs
Roaring at the crowd,
Along comes the lioness - looking really proud.

*Kurtis Shinner (9)*
*The Giffard Catholic School, Wolverhampton*


## THE SHARK AND THE FISH

On the boat I saw a shark, a great white shark,
Swimming round and round with glee after a little tea.

On the boat I saw a fish, a nice small fish
Swimming round and round another one, like he was rich.

On the boat I saw a shark and a fish,
Round and round they both went,
One after the other,
One after the other,
Round and round they went,
Shark, fish, shark, fish
Finally they met!

*Ciaran Treanor (10)*
*The Giffard Catholic School, Wolverhampton*

## TO SEE . . .

I must go down to the sea again, to the
lonely sea and sky,
To see the soft and silky waves to clitter
and clatter together.
To see the waves jump over the rocks and
throw the seaweed up.
For the seagulls to fly high in the sky and
touch the stars that shine so bright.
I like to see the sunset go,
With the dolphins and whales splashing
with their tails gliding together.

*Laura Finazzo (11)*
*The Giffard Catholic School, Wolverhampton*


## SEAGULLS

Gliding, gliding in the sky
Gliding, gliding very high
Getting faster I can't stop,
My wings are heavy, they might
drop off.
Getting closer to the ground,
travelling faster than light and sound.

*Ashley Rowe (11)*
*The Giffard Catholic School, Wolverhampton*

## WE'RE MICE!

We're not very tall
We're not big at all
In fact we are small . . .
We're mice.

We love to eat cheese
We never get fleas
We always say please . . .
We're mice.

We never would chat
To a cat or a rat, or a bat,
Come to that . . .
We're mice.

We all love the sun
Picnics are fun
Who'd like a bun?
We're mice.

Whenever it's snowing
Our ears will start glowing
To show where we're going . . .
We're mice.

We hope you will see and agree
That all we
As nice as can be . . .
We're mice!

*Nasrine Hermiz (9)*
*The Giffard Catholic School, Wolverhampton*

## I REMEMBER WHEN I WAS YOUNG . . .

I remember when I was young
A sunflower I was
We sang, we danced
Green cloth for my leaves and stem
A sunflower I was
My parents said I was a gem
A piece of card for the head
A sunflower I was
Sunflowers grow in a flower bed
We sang an *English Country Garden.*
A sunflower I was
I did not understand why the word
*Pardon* is in it.
Barbie doll I was given for being so good.
A sunflower I was
I seem to think I began in bud.

*Sinead Treanor  (9)*
*The Giffard Catholic School, Wolverhampton*

## FEELINGS

Scary, spooky houses
Dark, empty rooms.
All of these things scare me.
Do they scare you?

Lovely red roses
Big, shady trees.
All of these things make me happy
Do they make you happy?

The death of a Nan
The divorce of an aunt.
All of these things make me sad.
Do they make you sad too?

Scary, happy, sad or what,
All of these things happen in life,
I have feelings,
Do you have them too?

*Jennifer McCarthy (9)*
*The Giffard Catholic School, Wolverhampton*

## FRIENDS

Your friends are there when you need them
They stand by your side
They never run and hide
They always understand what you say
They never turn a blind eye.

So when your friend needs a helping hand
Don't just stand there
Help them!

Who is your *best* friend?
Have you turned a blind eye on *them?*
Are you there when they need *you?*
Because one day you will lose them,
Then you will know how much you liked them,
and it will be too late!

*Laura J Babbs (10)*
*Withymoor CP School, Brierley Hill*


## LAUGHING GAS

It makes you giggle
It makes you laugh,
It makes you wiggle
It makes you daft.
It makes you chuckle,
It's really funny
It makes you trip over your buckle,
It tickles your tummy.
Laughing gas
Oh!
Laughing gas!

*Lynsey Harris (10)*
*Withymoor CP School, Brierley Hill*

## MY BROTHER JAKE

I have a brother his name is Jake
He's so boring for goodness sake.
He's a massive pain and he's nasty to me
Loves only his PlayStation and his TV.

My brother mostly hates school
But thinks the Simpsons are cool.
He loves Pizza Hut
When he's there, he's a pain in the butt.

He's only nine
But acts like he's twenty-nine.
Bossing me around, thinking it's fine
All the time!

That's my brother Jake!

*Lauren Flavell (11)*
*Withymoor CP School, Brierley Hill*


## MY FRIENDS

They sand by you every day by day
They help you to work and play.
They never fall out with you
They always comfort you if something died or was lost.
They always understand,
They never run and hide.
They will never turn a blind eye on you
They will help you if you are in need,
They don't steal from you or lie to you,
They will never bully or turn away from you.

*How is your best friend?*

*Rachel Thompson (10)*
*Withymoor CP School, Brierley Hill*

## THE ROAD I TOOK . . .

One day I found myself in a wood
Where two roads diverged among the trees.
One was bare and trampled down
Many a person had crossed this road
The other was lush and green.
But many an obstacle was in this road
So this is the road I took.
I knew I would have to work hard
I tripped, I stumbled, I crossed a bridge
I came round a corner not knowing
What would be there.
I found a hill, so I climbed it
At the top I found the hardest part of my journey
But I was prepared for it.
I had worked hard
Life had been hard.
But my road was the right road.

*Ben Hough  (11)*
*Withymoor CP School, Brierley Hill*


## FOOTBALL

Oh football, oh football
Why are you so big
Oh football, oh football
Why do you have stripes?
Oh football, oh football
Why do you go so fast?
Oh football, oh football
Do you get headaches?
Oh football, oh football!

*Jason Bryan  (11)*
*Withymoor CP School, Brierley Hill*

## I SAW...

I saw a blazing tower
I saw a pretty flower

I saw blue seas
I saw green trees

I saw the sun in the sky
I saw the clouds flow by

I saw the winter snow
I saw the summer go

I saw a bottle of ale
I saw a weighing scale

I saw a dog and cat
I saw a scary bat

I saw a wooden door
I saw a very big saw

I saw a robot head
Then I woke up in my bed!

*Philip Batham (11)*
*Withymoor CP School, Brierley Hill*


## THE UNIVERSE

Shooting stars,
Milky Way,
Is all a part of the universe.
Aliens, distant planets
Is it true or not?

Are black holes true or not?
Do they really pull people in?
Does it really lead to another dimension?
Are they really black?

*Hayley Davies (11)*
*Withymoor CP School, Brierley Hill*

## I HAVE A DREAM . . .

I have a dream of a brilliant place
Where all God's creatures have a happy face.
Let all the fighting and wars end,
And a peaceful message we will send.

May painful pollution dissolve in a rushing race
but not in a grim, gradual, poor pace.
Let's keep the country glowing green,
So favourable flowers may be seen!

There shouldn't be any gluttony or greed
Everyone has a luxurious life to lead.
I hope love can spread,
Which brings wonderful wed.

Let this be a modern, fresh begin
And we shall live without any selfish sins.
My new generations shine through
Let's hope my millennium dreams come true!

*Lara Venables (10)*
*Withymoor CP School, Brierley Hill*

## MY WORST FEAR

They make me shiver with fright,
I hear them in my stomach every night.
My mom says 'They're fine.'
When I have them, a cold feeling runs down my spine.
My worst fear is,
*School dinners!*

**Joe Miles (10)**
**Withymoor CP School, Brierley Hill**


## WINTER

Winter is like an icy death
Winter is an exploding life force
Winter is an icy beast
Ice, frosty, winter
Winter is bleak
Winter is a savage.
Winter is lethal
Icy, frosty, winter.

**Terri-Anne Powell (9)**
**Withymoor CP School, Brierley Hill**


## HOUSE

H ouses are asleep through the night
O ver the hill and far away, waiting for the daytime to come
U nder the sunrise where the people start to rise
S chool are opening for the children to arrive
E veryone is happy his or her day play has begun
S oon be time for the sun to be gone.

*Louise Wood (10)*
*Withymoor CP School, Brierley Hill*

## THE JOURNEY OF LIFE

If I came to a fork in the road
I would pick the road with no
Bumps and no corners and no
Stones.
Not the road with a big hill and
Bricks and corners
The road I would take looks easy
But the road I would not take
looks hard.
Up the road I would take
there's a man there
Up the next lane there's a corner
And I don't know what's around
The corner
I turn the corner and there's a
Big hole and I have to turn back.

*Rhiannon Wood (11)*
*Withymoor CP School, Brierley Hill*


## TRAVELLING ALONG LIFE'S ROAD

Life's road may be easy, may be hard,
May be wide, may be thin,
You may have choices,
Left or right,
Up or down,
Straight or round,
Wide or thin,
Crossroads, forks
*Which will you take?*

*Joseph Hale (11)*
*Withymoor CP School, Brierley Hill*

## FIONA - THE TOMBOY

Fiona, my sister,
The world's biggest pain in the butt!
Has always been a Tomboy
Since the day she was brought.
For instance, have you ever met
A little girl quite cute.
Who, if you ever got close enough.
She'd punch you in the gut?
If you were unlucky
You'd get close enough to see
Fiona is a monster
Who practices on me!
There's only ever been
A little boy she likes
It was in playschool
At the time she had her first bike!
The little boy, Joshua, was quite a big hit
She loved him to pieces
And gave him a big kiss!
Later on in life, when Josh was dumped
She tried tomato soup
And loved it more than him!
It was tomato soup for breakfast
Tomato soup for tea
And then also, some in-between!
And now you know my sister,
How she is a pain.
What do you think -
Would you like to hit her with a cane?
I know I would!

*Paul Geary (11)*
*Withymoor CP School, Brierley Hill*

## The Nutritious Song

The nutritious song
Nothing is wrong,
If you listen to this song
You will end up as King Kong.

Carbohydrates are for ever
It's split up into starch and sugar,
Too much sugar is bad; it makes your teeth mad,
If you did not listen, you should be sad.

There're also proteins
That make you grow.
When you wake up you will go wow!
If you did not listen, you should go, oh no!

There're vitamins and minerals,
That make you strong,
And they make you long
If you did not listen, it is wrong.

There is water
Makes you like a motor
It's good for your blood
If you did not listen, you should put yourself in the mud.

There is fibre
It helps you digest
It finishes the test.
If you had not listened, you are not the best.

This is the end,
So remember this
When you eat
*The nutritious song!*

*Qasim Shafiq (10)*
*Withymoor CP School, Brierley Hill*

## BLINKY

His name is Blinky, he is a dope.
He has gigantic glasses.
As thick as a rope.
You might think he is clever.
You might think he is dumb.
Just check out the hairdo on his mum.
You might think he is small.
You might think he is tall.
But his head is really, really small.
When he goes outside,
He manages to make a mess,
But when you put his head on the bed . . .
He always stays up and never goes to bed.

*Jason Danks  (11)*
*Withymoor CP School, Brierley Hill*

## NIGHTMARES

They wait round every corner,
Under every pillow
Behind every cupboard,
And under every bed
Behind every door,
Where they're waiting there to catch you
If you don't know the score!

*Stephanie Hill  (10)*
*Withymoor CP School, Brierley Hill*

## THE TEST

The test is here
Once every year
I hope to do my best
So my brain can go to rest
When I get home
I'm all alone
Then suddenly a knock on the door
It's the test results
I've opened it up, I've passed
*Yes!*

**Richard Bayley  (11)**
**Withymoor CP School, Brierley Hill**


## PUPPIES

Puppies, puppies
Under there
Puppies are loveable
Playing in the dark
Young and they're warm
Silly and they're spotty
Their coats are glossy
They go to their kennels
And eat day and night
Puppies are not vicious
They never try to fight.

**Cheryl Haywood  (11)**
**Withymoor CP School, Brierley Hill**

## MY NOCTURNAL NUMBER 1

A soft, squidgy silk ball
A plump, pouched pet
A nut nibbler
A clever companion
A nice nocturnal
A fluffy, fun friend
A scurrying sweetheart
A perfect pet.

*Lucy Parsons  (11)*
*Withymoor CP School, Brierley Hill*


## MY LONG-EARED LOVE

A mystical sheet
A white fur ball
A chubby cheese lump
A lettuce vacuum
A soft silk sheet
An all-ears comforter
A pillow of velvet
A passionate pet.

*Nicola Hill  (10)*
*Withymoor CP School, Brierley Hill*

## THE WILD WIND

The wild wind is raging around the world,
Wrecking recreations and crushing churches.
The wild wind is a vile creature and should
not be allowed to walk the land.
Hurricanes, tornadoes wrecking the world,
A breeze is OK,
But hurricanes and tornadoes just blow us away.

*Christopher Morrey (11)*
*Withymoor CP School, Brierley Hill*


## MY FAVOURITE FRIEND

A friend for life
A nightmare killer
An armful of joy
A lifetime of love
A calming hand
A nightmare comforter
A bed warmer
A dark sky brightener
My favourite friend.

*Sarah Gordon (11)*
*Withymoor CP School, Brierley Hill*

## AUSTRALIA

Koalas swing in the shade of eucalyptus leaves,
Kangaroos leap along its sunny plains,
Minibeasts scurry across the sandy floor,
The duck-billed platypus dives in the cool waters,
Colourful birds swing from tree to tree,
Australia is the place to be.

*Chris Bates (10)*
*Withymoor CP School, Brierley Hill*


## HOT AIR BALLOONS

H   ot air balloons go,
O   ver the land,
T   o the place where the sun shines bright.

A   nywhere else in the world they go,
I    s awaiting a jolly good fright,
R   ight then, here we go, *up, up and away!*

B   ouncing away on
A   hot air balloon
L   iving, the world to be seen,
L   ittle old Susie
O   ver the land,
O   ver the sky and the sea
N   ever, never, never again,
S   aid Susie during her tea.

*Kerrie Short (10)*
*Woodfield Junior School*

## THE EMPEROR OF CALLAY

In a land far away
was a place called Callay
It was golden and rich but was made of clay
and every time it rained
the land squished and strained
and the emperor who reigned
was a man who was insane.

The man was insane,
'twas a pity he reigned
'cause he made a space rocket
to go into space.
It was slow and stubbed
and wasn't very good
but he managed to get up
and then he was up, up and away!

*Gem Blackburn (10)*
*Woodfield Junior School*


## UP, UP HIGH IN THE SKY

Up, up in the sky
Pigeons fly very high
Round the houses, round the tree
Flying high, flying free.

The pilots are wearing red, blue and white
Sharing cockpits ready to glide
Looking down at the multicoloured world.

Come on now let's go fly
Flying round the bright blue sky
Aeroplanes whiz past the white clouds.

*Rimpi Bhagat (11)*
*Woodfield Junior School*

## THE BIG BLUE BALLOON

There it is the big blue balloon,
Just standing there all droopy and let down.

I walk up to it and pull the string,
Suddenly it springs with life
And soon a big round blue balloon is in my garden.

I jump in and off I go just me and the big blue balloon,
Slowly up, up, higher and higher and then,
Silence, I'm above the clouds,
Slowly we drift past mountains and clouds,
Floating away,
The big blue balloon in the bright blue sky.

*Tom Nutting (11)*
*Woodfield Junior School*


## HOT AIR BALLOON

Floating around,
Head in the clouds,
Seeing what I can see.
I can see fields,
Big Ferris wheels
And one giant, ancient tree.

Drifting about,
Light as a cloud,
There's peace and quiet up high.
I drift over seas,
Forests of trees,
The sound of the wind in the sky.

*John Mills (11)*
*Woodfield Junior School*

## BUBBLES, BUBBLES

Bubbles, bubbles
Floating in the sky,
With swirls of rainbow patterns in them.
Bubbles, bubbles
They join hands *pop!*
And disappear into a world of their own.

*Nikkita Jirh  (10)*
*Woodfield Junior School*


## DRAGON

D  eadly fire spurts from his mouth,
R  oaring as he takes off,
A  gain he breathes out his fire,
G  radually disintegrating the clouds.
O  n and on he flies,
N  ever stopping till he dies.

*Ben Clark  (11)*
*Woodfield Junior School*


## BUBBLES

Floating softly in the sky
Rainbow colours swirl around
*Pop! Pop! Pop!*
They all disappear
Out of sight in another world.

*Catherine Shuttleworth  (10)*
*Woodfield Junior School*

## A Hot Air Balloon

A hot air balloon rises up from the deep depths of the world,
As you rise everything gets smaller and smaller
Until you can see micro machine cars
And human ants scurrying around.

Total silence . . . then *bang!*
A flame of glowing fire bursts out
Sending the balloon higher and then nothing,
The balloon soars higher gently and smoothly.

Another world has been born, clouds,
Giant pieces of white candyfloss,
Hilltops like the top of an ice-cream all snowy and cool

And then we float back down to earth
With a *kklumpth!*

*Luke Jones  (11)*
*Woodfield Junior School*


## Dreams

I wake up in the morning sun,
the dream's still in my mind,
I remember it in the morning,
by the afternoon it's faded.
Where do your dreams go, when they float out of your head,
do they fly into the sky to a place where nobody can remember?
But nightmares come back to haunt you
and they never quite go away, but happy dreams drift away,
to somewhere that no one can find them, ever, ever again.

*Rosie Allum  (11)*
*Woodfield Junior School*

## THE FLIGHT OF THE GREEN TUM BIRD

There was once a warm, wet rainforest,
In the magical land of Oroo,
With fire breathing worms and zadoobas
And castles and dingylaps too.

Now inside this warm, wet rainforest,
Sitting there on the branch of a tree,
Was the tiniest scrap of a green tum bird,
As cute and as small as can be.

He was flapping his small wings so hardly,
He was trying to fly, but in vain,
For he was all tired out from the effort,
And wet with the wind and the rain.

The poor little thing was so flustered
And sadly he let out a cry,
'Oh Mama, oh Papa, it's hopeless,
I'll never be able to fly!'

His Papa was quite sympathetic,
'Oh do cheer up son and rejoice!'
Till a big gust of wind blew right past him
And carried away his small voice.

Then the giant gust of wind blew his son off his perch
And he let out a great big *'Hooray!'*
For finally, at last, he was flying,
Up, up and away!

*Jessica Law  (11)*
*Woodfield Junior School*

## Up, Up And Away

Last night I dreamt of going into space
and dancing on the moon
I went skating on the Milky Way
and jumping on the moon.

I slid round the rings of Jupiter
I talked to some friendly aliens
who gave me milk and tea
but I said no 'cause I had to go home

But first I went on a shooting star
that took me to Saturn and Mars
then I said I really must go
Back to the planet Earth.

*Melanie Gibbons (11)*
*Woodfield Junior School*


## Hot Air Balloon

I'm flying high
up in the sky
looking down
and seeing
an array of colourful dots

The burner is lit,
I can't hear myself think
so I imagine I'm a bird
drifting away
into my own fantasy world.

*Rajdeep Aujla (11)*
*Woodfield Junior School*

# FLYING PIGS

In a part of the world,
That's yet to be found,
There comes a funny
Oinking sound.
From pink and black piggies,
With white and brown wings,
Who like to fly higher than high.

They run for take off,
Then fly rather high
And eventually bumping,
Into a great big thing in the sky (aeroplane).

People think that the poor ozone layer,
Is wrecked by pollution,
But really in our own minds we know,
That flying pigs are the solution.

But maybe one day when we wake up,
They'll have just . . . *gone!*

*Beth Hogan (10)*
*Woodfield Junior School*


# FIGHTER PILOT

I am a pilot whizzing along,
I see an enemy,
we exchange fire,
then he is gone.

*Joshua Power (11)*
*Woodfield Junior School*

# THE EAGLE

The eagle flies above the Earth, looking for food to eat.
He swoops down from the sky and catches a mouse with his feet.
He goes back to feed his young but then he smells some terrible dung.
He falls right out of the sky
and then he loses his mousy pie.

When he recovered from his fall, his little 'uns in the nest
were 'avin' a ball.
When he returned without any food
his babies stripped him totally nude.
They told him to go back out and hunt
or else he was a real runt.
They told him to go or else they would,
make him into an eagle pud.
Just when the chicks were about to act
the mother arrived and began to distract.
The babies were about to kill their dad
but then the mother got really mad.
She sent them to bed without any tea
and then she said 'They take advantage of me.'

*Mitchell Crane  (10)*
*Woodfield Junior School*


# BUBBLES

The bubbles floated high,
Higher and higher up in the sky
Floating like free molecules
As light as the smallest feather
Then they go *pop*
The tiny water drops fall
Like thunderbolts.

*Harnish Ubhi  (11)*
*Woodfield Junior School*

## THE RAF SEA KING

Trapped at sea, no hope for me,
call the lifeguard, help me please!
We're on a quest, to save the rest,
swooping low, like a river on the flow.
*Heed the calls of the sea king!*

My boat has sunk and so's our luck.
Hey! Here's a helicopter, to save my life!
Here's the casualty, now let me see,
there's a place to land, now to airlift him to the sand.
I'm going to be saved!

*Up, up and away!*

***Andrew Shannon-Little (11)***
***Woodfield Junior School***


## HOT AIR BALLOONS

Floating around in a sky of blue,
Showing its patterns to me and you,
Gently swaying from side to side,
Holding its passengers safely inside,
Never again was the sky so peaceful,
With its flame glowing bright the sky is never dull,
Passing the clouds as it flies,
Filling the deep blue skies,
Now down here on the people's Earth,
A new dream has its birth.

***Kirsty Preston (11)***
***Woodfield Junior School***

## MY DREAM OF AN AEROPLANE

There are aeroplanes flying overhead
I'm waving
They can't see me
It's as if I were dead

I want them to see me
I could fly so high
If they asked me to join them
On their mission up in the sky

I could fly in the sky
So very very high
I'd see the moon and the sun
I'd have ever so much fun

I could see all the shapes of the clouds
Yes I would
If the aeroplanes up there
Would only see me

They're flying past
I'm running very fast
They're moving on over the pasture
Next time I'll have to run faster

So now I'm very upset
Because I didn't get
What I wanted
So now I'll cry.

***Emma Chapman (10)***
***Woodfield Junior School***

## NEAR THE PLANET MARS

Somewhere near the planet Mars,
A man in his spaceship flew through the stars,
It landed on the planet Mars
And he had a look around.

He saw a monster and he looked rather hot,
So he hid behind a flower pot,
The monster growled 'Whose ship is this
It's standing on my plant called Fiss.'

He ran from behind the flower pot,
Jumped in his spaceship and took off,
*Up, up and away!*

*Katherine Lee  (10)*
*Woodfield Junior School*

## SPACE

S    pace is a wonderful thing.
      When I grow up I'm going to be an astronaut.
P    luto, Venus and Mars, all the exciting planets,
      I will visit them on my journey.
A    liens live in space, most aliens come to Earth in
      UFOs.
C    oloured planets are all lined up together in space.
      They are all bright and fantastic.
E    veryone wants to go up in space and become an
      astronaut, especially me!

*James Brown  (11)*
*Woodfield Junior School*

## HOT AIR BALLOONS

In a hot air balloon,
Up, up and away,
Floating this morning,
Floating all day.

Peaceful and quiet,
Until all of a sudden,
It is a roar of the fire,
We are going up, up,
But now we are going higher.

Floating up high,
Is that the time?
It's time to go down.

I've seen the houses,
I've seen the town hall,
I've seen the people,
Now they are small.

We are going down,
No time to stop,
Slowly and quietly,
We gently drop.

*Adam Cook (11)*
*Woodfield Junior School*


## BUBBLES

3D circles floating around,
With rainbows inside,
Light as a feather.

If I was that size and weight,
I would mix with the others,
I would float about.

Then someone will poke me
And I will disappear,
Into thin air.

Bubbles floating . . .
*Up, up and away!*

**Serena Chander (11)**
**Woodfield Junior School**

## BLAST-OFF

5, 4, 3, 2, 1
blast-off!

The rocket starts to go high
it'll be a holiday
up in the sky
as I go away.

I go past the stars
I'm going to the moon,
but not Mars,
I hope I get there by noon.

I'm up in space,
on the moon,
but it's hard to keep a pace
so I'll eat the cheese with my spoon.

Now it's time to go home
tidy my room,
listen to Dad moan,
but I'll still think about the moon.

**Rachael Boyes (10)**
**Woodfield Junior School**

## UP, UP AND AWAY

Up, up and away I want to stay
floating in the air
with my dazzling hair,
playing with the birds and herding them
up, up and away.
I fly in the air
I fly everywhere,
but I don't fly in the clouds
it doesn't make me proud
it's too damp and wet
and don't forget
to look out for me.

*David Augustus (11)*
*Woodfield Junior School*

## BUBBLETASTIC

It starts as water like a load of rubble,
Blow it and it turns into a massive bubble,
Then it floats into the sky
And says to the water 'I'll miss you bye-bye.
I want to go really high
And reach the top of the sky
But when I reach the very top
I'm surely going to pop.'

*Tim Francis (10)*
*Woodfield Junior School*

## BUTTERFLIES

Butterflies, butterflies
everywhere
fluttering, fluttering
over there.
Twinkle, twinkle
around my hair
oh I wish I could be with you
in the light and bright air.

*Laura Nightingale  (9)*
*Woodlands Primary School*


## MY LITTLE SISTER

My little sister is a pain
When she makes a mess and it wasn't me
I always get the blame.
My little sister is never as good as gold
Absolutely trashes the place
I wish she'd do as she's *told!*

*Elizabeth Whelan  (8)*
*Woodlands Primary School*


## BUTTERFLY

Butterfly, butterfly, you fly so high in the sky,
you can fly to the clouds up above,
the wind will blow and you will go up, up and away,
flying in the sky, bye-bye butterfly.

*Alice Whittome & Aimee Treble  (8)*
*Woodthorne Primary School*

## WHAT A WONDERFUL WATER WORLD

Water, water, what a wonderful water world
There could be in the deep blue sea
Look at the people that swim in the sea
Oh how I wish it could be me
To go on the adventure that I long
To hear the sea sing its beautiful song.
I watch lots of water programmes on TV
But they're not as good as I want to see
To see the blue dolphins swim with grace
Look at the fish's swimming pace.
To see the green seaweed sway all day
Look at the seals I wonder what they play
Swimming all day in a school
It is really that cool.

It certainly would be cool to swim in the deep blue sea
In a wonderful *water world.*

*Kathryn Vickers  (8)*
*Woodthorne Primary School*


## MUM'S GONE CRAZY

Mum's gone crazy, she's absolutely mad
She's grown a long green tail, it makes us really sad.
She won't let us have any sweets, she's really, really mean,
She gets really cross at times, she's the worst mum you've ever seen.
But when she's calmed down a bit her tail disappears,
Now we've made friends, so wipe away those tears!

*Melanie Hartness  (8)*
*Woodthorne Primary School*

## 2000

The year 2000 will be a wonderful time
Everyone'll go mad when the clock starts to chime
There'll be fireworks and parties and everyone'll be happy
Because it's a new millennium and the other years were crappy
There'll be dancing and singing and drinking and laughter
But everyone'll have hangovers the morning after
The children will be screaming and jumping that morning
But the parents will be tired so they'll just lay in bed yawning
There'll be lots of resolutions that no one will keep
Let us not forget that talk is cheap
Kids are to help and tidy up (puff not a chance)
And others are to be more lively like to sing and dance
So there you have it the year 2000
Some people say it is going to be the end
And we will not see another one
Because by then we'll all be gone.

*Hayley Willetts (11)*
*Woodthorne Primary School*


## MY OWN WORLD

Leaves for trees were candyfloss
and broccoli was used for all the moss.
Middles of flowers were lollipops
and all the stars were bottle tops.
Chocolate was used for bark on trees
and the sun was made from cheese.
Flower petals were made from apple
and on my world everybody cackled.
Oh how I wish this world could be
an extraordinary world made just for me!

*Laura Walpole (8)*
*Woodthorne Primary School*

## MY MUM

Roses are red,
Violets are blue,
Grass is green
And I really miss you.

Thank you for the food
you gave me,
I cry in the night,
Just for you.

When you gave me treats,
I felt like giving you sweets,

But when you died,
Everything changed.
I felt like screaming
Very loud.

I miss you Mother,
I will always remember you
And the love you gave me
Thank you!

*Jean Hughes (11)*
*Woodthorne Primary School*


## WASHING

What is all the washing about
Every day, week in, week out?
From getting up till going to bed,
I'm tired of hearing the same thing said.
Whether the water is cold or hot,
Whether I like it or whether I don't,
Whether I will or whether I won't -
'Have you washed your hands and face?'
I seem to live in the washing place.

Whenever I go for a walk or a ride,
As soon as I put my nose inside
The door again, there's someone there
With a sponge and soap and a lot they care
If I have something better to do,
'No wash your face and your fingers too.'
Before a meal is ever begun
And after ever a meal is done,
It's time to turn on the water spout.

Please, what is all the washing about?

*Priscilla Yisa  (10)*
*Woodthorne Primary School*


## CATS AND KITTENS

So soft and gentle
Living under a tree
Purring sweetly
As the wind sways smoothly.

Quietly and soundless
He wears his silk coat
Sleeping like a baby
With his eyes shut tight.

He awakens
Stretches without a sound
He moves gracefully
Ready to find another sleeping spot.

*Laura Cotterill  (11)*
*Woodthorne Primary School*

## A Bit Scary

Going up the stairs
Hear a sound,
Creak
What is it?
There it goes again
Creak.

Getting into bed
What's that on the ceiling?
It's moving
Getting closer
It's right above me now
What is it?

The middle of the night
Can't get to sleep,
There's a scary grin on the wall
What is it?
I don't like it
Phew it's morning, glad to be out of the dark.

*Libby Ratcliffe (8)*
*Woodthorne Primary School*


## Litter

L   itter should be in a bin
I    always make sure I put it in
T   o and fro the litter goes
T   o and fro when the wind blows
E   veryone should put it in
R   ight where it belongs, in a bin.

*Amelia Taylor (8)*
*Woodthorne Primary School*